www.Testinar.com

... So Much More Online!

✓ FREE Math lessons

✓ More Math learning books!

✓ Mathematics Worksheets

✓ Online Math Tutors

Need a PDF version of this book?

Please visit www.Testinar.com

TASC Math

Practice Workbook

2020-2021

Abundant Skill-Building Math Exercises

and 2 Full-Length TASC Math Practice Tests

By

Jay Daie & Reza Nazari

All inquiries should be addressed to:

info@Testinar.com

www.Testinar.com

ISBN: 978-1-64612-455-8

Published by: Testinar Inc

www.Testinar.com

Visit www.Testinar.com

for Online Math Practice

Description

TASC Math Practice Workbook 2020-2021, which reflects the 2020-2021 test guidelines, represents abundant Math exercises, sample TASC Math questions, and quizzes with answers and detailed solutions to help you hone your math skills, overcome your exam anxiety, boost your confidence—and do your best to succeed on the TASC Math test. This is a precious math exercise book for TASC test-takers who need extra practice in math to ace the TASC Math test. Upon completion of this comprehensive math workbook, you will have a solid foundation and sufficient practice to defeat the TASC Math test. **This comprehensive practice book is your ticket to scoring higher on TASC Math.**

TASC Math Practice Workbook 2020-2021 with over 3,500 sample questions and over 8,000 online math questions will help you fully prepare for the TASC Math test. Two full-length and realistic TASC Math practice tests with detailed answers and explanations that reflect the format and question types on the TASC are provided to check your exam-readiness and identify where you need more practice.

This comprehensive math workbook contains many exciting and unique features to help you improve your TASC Math test score, including:

- ✓ Content 100% aligned with the 2020 TASC test
- ✓ Complete coverage of all TASC Math concepts and topics which you will be tested
- ✓ Abundant Math skill-building exercises to help test-takers approach different question types that might be unfamiliar to them
- ✓ Over 8,000 additional TASC math online practice questions in both multiple-choice and grid-in formats with answers grouped by topic, so you can focus on your weak areas
- ✓ 2 full-length practice tests (featuring new question types) with detailed answers

This TASC Math practice workbook and other Testinar books are used by thousands of students each year to help them review core content areas, brush-up in math, discover their strengths and weaknesses, and achieve their best scores on the TASC test.

Contents

✏️ **Find the missing number.**

1) $850 - \_\_\_ = 580$

2) $770 + \_\_\_ = 1170$

3) $240 + \_\_\_ = 580$

4) $940 + \_\_\_ = 1370$

5) $810 + \_\_\_ = 1420$

6) $460 + \_\_\_ = 1350$

7) $560 + \_\_\_ = 1460$

8) $470 + \_\_\_ = 940$

9) $890 + \_\_\_ = 1230$

10) $960 - \_\_\_ = 210$

✏️ **Solve.**

1) $\begin{array}{r} 4,324 \\ -\ 3,604 \\ \hline \end{array}$

2) $\begin{array}{r} 1,786 \\ +\ \ \ 689 \\ \hline \end{array}$

3) $\begin{array}{r} 4,559 \\ -\ \ \ 583 \\ \hline \end{array}$

4) $\begin{array}{r} 3,337 \\ -\ 3,127 \\ \hline \end{array}$

5) $\begin{array}{r} 3,816 \\ +\ \ \ 940 \\ \hline \end{array}$

6) $\begin{array}{r} 3,760 \\ -\ 3,286 \\ \hline \end{array}$

7) $\begin{array}{r} 4,770 \\ -\ 2,021 \\ \hline \end{array}$

8) $\begin{array}{r} 4,559 \\ +\ 4,346 \\ \hline \end{array}$

9) $\begin{array}{r} 3,763 \\ +\ 1,786 \\ \hline \end{array}$

10) $\begin{array}{r} 4,876 \\ +\ \ \ 564 \\ \hline \end{array}$

11) $\begin{array}{r} 4,465 \\ +\ 1,749 \\ \hline \end{array}$

12) $\begin{array}{r} 3,666 \\ +\ 1,378 \\ \hline \end{array}$

3

✏️ **Find the missing number.**

1) $850 - 270 = 580$

2) $770 + 400 = 1170$

3) $240 + 340 = 580$

4) $940 + 430 = 1370$

5) $810 + 610 = 1420$

6) $460 + 890 = 1350$

7) $560 + 900 = 1460$

8) $470 + 470 = 940$

9) $890 + 340 = 1230$

10) $960 - 750 = 210$

✏️ **Solve.**

1)
$$\begin{array}{r} 4,324 \\ -\ 3,604 \\ \hline 720 \end{array}$$

2)
$$\begin{array}{r} 1,786 \\ +\ \ \ 689 \\ \hline 2,475 \end{array}$$

3)
$$\begin{array}{r} 4,559 \\ -\ \ \ 583 \\ \hline 3,976 \end{array}$$

4)
$$\begin{array}{r} 3,337 \\ -\ 3,127 \\ \hline 210 \end{array}$$

5)
$$\begin{array}{r} 3,816 \\ +\ \ \ 940 \\ \hline 4,756 \end{array}$$

6)
$$\begin{array}{r} 3,760 \\ -\ 3,286 \\ \hline 474 \end{array}$$

7)
$$\begin{array}{r} 4,770 \\ -\ 2,021 \\ \hline 2,749 \end{array}$$

8)
$$\begin{array}{r} 4,559 \\ +\ 4,346 \\ \hline 8,905 \end{array}$$

9)
$$\begin{array}{r} 3,763 \\ +\ 1,786 \\ \hline 5,549 \end{array}$$

10)
$$\begin{array}{r} 4,876 \\ +\ \ \ 564 \\ \hline 5,440 \end{array}$$

11)
$$\begin{array}{r} 4,465 \\ +\ 1,749 \\ \hline 6,214 \end{array}$$

12)
$$\begin{array}{r} 3,666 \\ +\ 1,378 \\ \hline 5,044 \end{array}$$

✏️ **Calculate.**

1) $828 \div 36 =$

2) $10 \times 10 =$

3) $350 \div 25 =$

4) $3780 \div 84 =$

5) $46 \times 32 =$

6) $28028 \div 98 =$

7) $4402 \div 71 =$

8) $20856 \div 24 =$

9) $7854 \div 51 =$

10) $1012 \times 60 =$

11) $10153 \div 71 =$

12) $1952 \div 32 =$

13) $697 \div 41 =$

14) $330 \times 48 =$

15) $58 \times 52 =$

16) $1152 \div 24 =$

17) $910 \div 14 =$

18) $473 \times 24 =$

19) $1078 \times 15 =$

20) $352 \times 75 =$

21) $44 \times 38 =$

22) $95 \times 77 =$

23) $8099 \div 91 =$

24) $2945 \div 31 =$

25) $22264 \div 44 =$

26) $20460 \div 60 =$

27) $902 \times 22 =$

28) $363 \times 64 =$

29) $38775 \div 75 =$

30) $90 \times 31 =$

✏️ **Calculate.**

1) $828 \div 36 = 23$

2) $10 \times 10 = 100$

3) $350 \div 25 = 14$

4) $3780 \div 84 = 45$

5) $46 \times 32 = 1472$

6) $28028 \div 98 = 286$

7) $4402 \div 71 = 62$

8) $20856 \div 24 = 869$

9) $7854 \div 51 = 154$

10) $1012 \times 60 = 60720$

11) $10153 \div 71 = 143$

12) $1952 \div 32 = 61$

13) $697 \div 41 = 17$

14) $330 \times 48 = 15840$

15) $58 \times 52 = 3016$

16) $1152 \div 24 = 48$

17) $910 \div 14 = 65$

18) $473 \times 24 = 11352$

19) $1078 \times 15 = 16170$

20) $352 \times 75 = 26400$

21) $44 \times 38 = 1672$

22) $95 \times 77 = 7315$

23) $8099 \div 91 = 89$

24) $2945 \div 31 = 95$

25) $22264 \div 44 = 506$

26) $20460 \div 60 = 341$

27) $902 \times 22 = 19844$

28) $363 \times 64 = 23232$

29) $38775 \div 75 = 517$

30) $90 \times 31 = 2790$

Simplifying Fractions

✏️ **Simplify the fractions.**

1) $\frac{80}{95} =$ 2) $\frac{70}{105} =$ 3) $\frac{9}{12} =$

4) $\frac{45}{48} =$ 5) $\frac{70}{85} =$ 6) $\frac{30}{51} =$

7) $\frac{39}{60} =$ 8) $\frac{50}{85} =$ 9) $\frac{39}{48} =$

10) $\frac{42}{63} =$ 11) $\frac{15}{30} =$ 12) $\frac{75}{110} =$

13) $\frac{95}{110} =$ 14) $\frac{55}{70} =$ 15) $\frac{48}{69} =$

16) $\frac{15}{18} =$ 17) $\frac{25}{40} =$ 18) $\frac{50}{65} =$

19) $\frac{85}{120} =$ 20) $\frac{30}{33} =$ 21) $\frac{12}{21} =$

22) $\frac{45}{60} =$ 23) $\frac{45}{66} =$ 24) $\frac{40}{75} =$

25) $\frac{57}{78} =$ 26) $\frac{18}{39} =$ 27) $\frac{27}{36} =$

28) $\frac{60}{75} =$ 29) $\frac{90}{125} =$ 30) $\frac{45}{54} =$

31) $\frac{100}{135} =$ 32) $\frac{30}{39} =$ 33) $\frac{36}{57} =$

✏️ **Simplify the fractions.**

1) $\frac{80}{95} = \frac{16}{19}$

2) $\frac{70}{105} = \frac{14}{21}$

3) $\frac{9}{12} = \frac{3}{4}$

4) $\frac{45}{48} = \frac{15}{16}$

5) $\frac{70}{85} = \frac{14}{17}$

6) $\frac{30}{51} = \frac{10}{17}$

7) $\frac{39}{60} = \frac{13}{20}$

8) $\frac{50}{85} = \frac{10}{17}$

9) $\frac{39}{48} = \frac{13}{16}$

10) $\frac{42}{63} = \frac{14}{21}$

11) $\frac{15}{30} = \frac{3}{6}$

12) $\frac{75}{110} = \frac{15}{22}$

13) $\frac{95}{110} = \frac{19}{22}$

14) $\frac{55}{70} = \frac{11}{14}$

15) $\frac{48}{69} = \frac{16}{23}$

16) $\frac{15}{18} = \frac{5}{6}$

17) $\frac{25}{40} = \frac{5}{8}$

18) $\frac{50}{65} = \frac{10}{13}$

19) $\frac{85}{120} = \frac{17}{24}$

20) $\frac{30}{33} = \frac{10}{11}$

21) $\frac{12}{21} = \frac{4}{7}$

22) $\frac{45}{60} = \frac{9}{12}$

23) $\frac{45}{66} = \frac{15}{22}$

24) $\frac{40}{75} = \frac{8}{15}$

25) $\frac{57}{78} = \frac{19}{26}$

26) $\frac{18}{39} = \frac{6}{13}$

27) $\frac{27}{36} = \frac{9}{12}$

28) $\frac{60}{75} = \frac{12}{15}$

29) $\frac{90}{125} = \frac{18}{25}$

30) $\frac{45}{54} = \frac{15}{18}$

31) $\frac{100}{135} = \frac{20}{27}$

32) $\frac{30}{39} = \frac{10}{13}$

33) $\frac{36}{57} = \frac{12}{19}$

✏️ **Solve.**

1) $\frac{9}{9} + \frac{7}{2} =$

2) $\frac{7}{9} + \frac{7}{3} =$

3) $\frac{6}{6} + \frac{6}{2} =$

4) $\frac{15}{9} + \frac{11}{11} =$

5) $\frac{11}{9} + \frac{11}{10} =$

6) $\frac{13}{14} + \frac{15}{15} =$

7) $\frac{14}{9} + \frac{13}{14} =$

8) $\frac{8}{8} + \frac{11}{12} =$

9) $\frac{9}{8} + \frac{8}{2} =$

10) $\frac{13}{12} + \frac{18}{11} =$

11) $\frac{12}{8} + \frac{12}{13} =$

12) $\frac{9}{4} + \frac{8}{4} =$

13) $\frac{8}{7} + \frac{4}{4} =$

14) $\frac{10}{12} + \frac{16}{17} =$

15) $\frac{14}{15} + \frac{18}{10} =$

✏️ **Solve.**

1) $\frac{8}{6} - \frac{1}{3} =$

2) $\frac{8}{5} - \frac{1}{8} =$

3) $\frac{17}{7} - \frac{17}{16} =$

4) $\frac{15}{11} - \frac{18}{16} =$

5) $\frac{18}{10} - \frac{16}{17} =$

6) $\frac{7}{4} - \frac{6}{5} =$

7) $\frac{6}{3} - \frac{4}{4} =$

8) $\frac{6}{8} - \frac{2}{3} =$

9) $\frac{15}{12} - \frac{11}{12} =$

10) $\frac{17}{5} - \frac{14}{13} =$

11) $\frac{6}{3} - \frac{5}{5} =$

12) $\frac{8}{3} - \frac{6}{4} =$

13) $\frac{5}{2} - \frac{3}{2} =$

14) $\frac{21}{2} - \frac{15}{18} =$

15) $\frac{24}{3} - \frac{12}{18} =$

16) $\frac{7}{5} - \frac{7}{7} =$

17) $\frac{5}{4} - \frac{3}{6} =$

18) $\frac{24}{4} - \frac{17}{14} =$

Answers of Adding and Subtracting Fractions

✏️ **Solve.**

1) $\frac{9}{9} + \frac{7}{2} = \frac{9}{2}$

2) $\frac{7}{9} + \frac{7}{3} = \frac{28}{9}$

3) $\frac{6}{6} + \frac{6}{2} = \frac{4}{1}$

4) $\frac{15}{9} + \frac{11}{11} = \frac{8}{3}$

5) $\frac{11}{9} + \frac{11}{10} = \frac{209}{90}$

6) $\frac{13}{14} + \frac{15}{15} = \frac{27}{14}$

7) $\frac{14}{9} + \frac{13}{14} = \frac{313}{126}$

8) $\frac{8}{8} + \frac{11}{12} = \frac{23}{12}$

9) $\frac{9}{8} + \frac{8}{2} = \frac{41}{8}$

10) $\frac{13}{12} + \frac{18}{11} = \frac{359}{132}$

11) $\frac{12}{8} + \frac{12}{13} = \frac{63}{26}$

12) $\frac{9}{4} + \frac{8}{4} = \frac{17}{4}$

13) $\frac{8}{7} + \frac{4}{4} = \frac{15}{7}$

14) $\frac{10}{12} + \frac{16}{17} = \frac{181}{102}$

15) $\frac{14}{15} + \frac{18}{10} = \frac{41}{15}$

✏️ **Solve.**

1) $\frac{8}{6} - \frac{1}{3} = \frac{1}{1}$

2) $\frac{8}{5} - \frac{1}{8} = \frac{59}{40}$

3) $\frac{17}{7} - \frac{17}{16} = \frac{153}{112}$

4) $\frac{15}{11} - \frac{18}{16} = \frac{21}{88}$

5) $\frac{18}{10} - \frac{16}{17} = \frac{73}{85}$

6) $\frac{7}{4} - \frac{6}{5} = \frac{11}{20}$

7) $\frac{6}{3} - \frac{4}{4} = \frac{1}{1}$

8) $\frac{6}{8} - \frac{2}{3} = \frac{1}{12}$

9) $\frac{15}{12} - \frac{11}{12} = \frac{1}{3}$

10) $\frac{17}{5} - \frac{14}{13} = \frac{151}{65}$

11) $\frac{6}{3} - \frac{5}{5} = \frac{1}{1}$

12) $\frac{8}{3} - \frac{6}{4} = \frac{7}{6}$

13) $\frac{5}{2} - \frac{3}{2} = \frac{1}{1}$

14) $\frac{21}{2} - \frac{15}{18} = \frac{29}{3}$

15) $\frac{24}{3} - \frac{12}{18} = \frac{22}{3}$

16) $\frac{7}{5} - \frac{7}{7} = \frac{2}{5}$

17) $\frac{5}{4} - \frac{3}{6} = \frac{3}{4}$

18) $\frac{24}{4} - \frac{17}{14} = \frac{67}{14}$

10

✏️ **Multiply the fractions and simplify if needed.**

1) $\frac{9}{9} \times \frac{11}{15} =$

2) $\frac{3}{5} \times \frac{13}{15} =$

3) $\frac{5}{3} \times \frac{13}{11} =$

4) $\frac{9}{7} \times \frac{6}{5} =$

5) $\frac{6}{10} \times \frac{4}{7} =$

6) $\frac{9}{7} \times \frac{15}{18} =$

7) $\frac{4}{5} \times \frac{6}{4} =$

8) $\frac{2}{2} \times \frac{8}{4} =$

9) $\frac{4}{6} \times \frac{18}{17} =$

10) $\frac{5}{3} \times \frac{5}{4} =$

11) $\frac{8}{10} \times \frac{7}{1} =$

12) $\frac{8}{2} \times \frac{17}{13} =$

13) $\frac{2}{3} \times \frac{4}{1} =$

14) $\frac{3}{4} \times \frac{11}{12} =$

15) $\frac{8}{6} \times \frac{15}{17} =$

✏️ **Dividing fractions. Then simplify.**

1) $\frac{8}{8} \div \frac{7}{2} =$

2) $\frac{6}{9} \div \frac{8}{4} =$

3) $\frac{6}{4} \div \frac{7}{6} =$

4) $\frac{5}{4} \div \frac{3}{6} =$

5) $\frac{7}{9} \div \frac{1}{8} =$

6) $\frac{8}{2} \div \frac{5}{5} =$

7) $\frac{9}{8} \div \frac{5}{4} =$

8) $\frac{8}{4} \div \frac{8}{7} =$

9) $\frac{7}{4} \div \frac{3}{1} =$

10) $\frac{9}{5} \div \frac{2}{3} =$

11) $\frac{3}{4} \div \frac{2}{1} =$

12) $\frac{3}{3} \div \frac{3}{3} =$

13) $\frac{8}{6} \div \frac{6}{7} =$

14) $\frac{2}{5} \div \frac{1}{7} =$

15) $\frac{6}{7} \div \frac{5}{6} =$

16) $\frac{2}{2} \div \frac{8}{1} =$

17) $\frac{3}{5} \div \frac{6}{3} =$

18) $\frac{8}{10} \div \frac{8}{3} =$

▶ Multiply the fractions and simplify if needed.

1) $\frac{9}{9} \times \frac{11}{15} = \frac{11}{15}$

2) $\frac{3}{5} \times \frac{13}{15} = \frac{13}{25}$

3) $\frac{5}{3} \times \frac{13}{11} = \frac{65}{33}$

4) $\frac{9}{7} \times \frac{6}{5} = \frac{54}{35}$

5) $\frac{6}{10} \times \frac{4}{7} = \frac{12}{35}$

6) $\frac{9}{7} \times \frac{15}{18} = \frac{15}{14}$

7) $\frac{4}{5} \times \frac{6}{4} = \frac{6}{5}$

8) $\frac{2}{2} \times \frac{8}{4} = \frac{2}{1}$

9) $\frac{4}{6} \times \frac{18}{17} = \frac{12}{17}$

10) $\frac{5}{3} \times \frac{5}{4} = \frac{25}{12}$

11) $\frac{8}{10} \times \frac{7}{1} = \frac{28}{5}$

12) $\frac{8}{2} \times \frac{17}{13} = \frac{68}{13}$

13) $\frac{2}{3} \times \frac{4}{1} = \frac{8}{3}$

14) $\frac{3}{4} \times \frac{11}{12} = \frac{11}{16}$

15) $\frac{8}{6} \times \frac{15}{17} = \frac{20}{17}$

▶ Dividing fractions. Then simplify.

1) $\frac{8}{8} \div \frac{7}{2} = \frac{2}{7}$

2) $\frac{6}{9} \div \frac{8}{4} = \frac{1}{3}$

3) $\frac{6}{4} \div \frac{7}{6} = \frac{9}{7}$

4) $\frac{5}{4} \div \frac{3}{6} = \frac{5}{2}$

5) $\frac{7}{9} \div \frac{1}{8} = \frac{56}{9}$

6) $\frac{8}{2} \div \frac{5}{5} = \frac{4}{1}$

7) $\frac{9}{8} \div \frac{5}{4} = \frac{9}{10}$

8) $\frac{8}{4} \div \frac{8}{7} = \frac{7}{4}$

9) $\frac{7}{4} \div \frac{3}{1} = \frac{7}{12}$

10) $\frac{9}{5} \div \frac{2}{3} = \frac{27}{10}$

11) $\frac{3}{4} \div \frac{2}{1} = \frac{3}{8}$

12) $\frac{3}{3} \div \frac{3}{3} = \frac{1}{1} = 1$

13) $\frac{8}{6} \div \frac{6}{7} = \frac{14}{9}$

14) $\frac{2}{5} \div \frac{1}{7} = \frac{14}{5}$

15) $\frac{6}{7} \div \frac{5}{6} = \frac{36}{35}$

16) $\frac{2}{2} \div \frac{8}{1} = \frac{1}{8}$

17) $\frac{3}{5} \div \frac{6}{3} = \frac{3}{10}$

18) $\frac{8}{10} \div \frac{8}{3} = \frac{3}{10}$

✏️ **Solve.**

1) $4\frac{6}{2} + 7\frac{2}{4} =$

2) $4\frac{2}{2} + 5\frac{5}{2} =$

3) $4\frac{8}{10} + 3\frac{7}{1} =$

4) $2\frac{5}{2} + 4\frac{7}{3} =$

5) $4\frac{5}{10} + 2\frac{4}{4} =$

6) $7\frac{7}{10} + 1\frac{7}{1} =$

7) $6\frac{9}{8} + 2\frac{2}{1} =$

8) $2\frac{3}{5} + 6\frac{6}{1} =$

9) $1\frac{8}{8} + 1\frac{4}{7} =$

10) $6\frac{3}{10} + 8\frac{6}{5} =$

11) $3\frac{6}{5} + 3\frac{4}{1} =$

12) $4\frac{4}{2} + 7\frac{1}{3} =$

13) $8\frac{9}{2} + 3\frac{7}{1} =$

14) $6\frac{9}{6} + 5\frac{2}{6} =$

15) $2\frac{10}{7} + 1\frac{2}{4} =$

16) $5\frac{9}{9} + 1\frac{3}{8} =$

17) $1\frac{3}{6} + 5\frac{5}{2} =$

18) $2\frac{10}{6} + 4\frac{3}{7} =$

19) $1\frac{5}{3} + 7\frac{2}{6} =$

20) $2\frac{7}{5} + 5\frac{1}{6} =$

21) $2\frac{5}{4} + 5\frac{4}{1} =$

22) $2\frac{9}{3} + 6\frac{2}{2} =$

✏️ **Solve.**

1) $4\frac{6}{2} + 7\frac{2}{4} = = 14\frac{1}{2}$

2) $4\frac{2}{2} + 5\frac{5}{2} = = 12\frac{1}{2}$

3) $4\frac{8}{10} + 3\frac{7}{1} = = 14\frac{4}{5}$

4) $2\frac{5}{2} + 4\frac{7}{3} = = 10\frac{5}{6}$

5) $4\frac{5}{10} + 2\frac{4}{4} = = 7\frac{1}{2}$

6) $7\frac{7}{10} + 1\frac{7}{1} = = 15\frac{7}{10}$

7) $6\frac{9}{8} + 2\frac{2}{1} = = 11\frac{1}{8}$

8) $2\frac{3}{5} + 6\frac{6}{1} = = 14\frac{3}{5}$

9) $1\frac{8}{8} + 1\frac{4}{7} = = 3\frac{4}{7}$

10) $6\frac{3}{10} + 8\frac{6}{5} = = 15\frac{1}{2}$

11) $3\frac{6}{5} + 3\frac{4}{1} = = 11\frac{1}{5}$

12) $4\frac{4}{2} + 7\frac{1}{3} = = 13\frac{1}{3}$

13) $8\frac{9}{2} + 3\frac{7}{1} = = 22\frac{1}{2}$

14) $6\frac{9}{6} + 5\frac{2}{6} = = 12\frac{5}{6}$

15) $2\frac{10}{7} + 1\frac{2}{4} = = 4\frac{13}{14}$

16) $5\frac{9}{9} + 1\frac{3}{8} = = 7\frac{3}{8}$

17) $1\frac{3}{6} + 5\frac{5}{2} = = 9\frac{0}{1}$

18) $2\frac{10}{6} + 4\frac{3}{7} = = 8\frac{2}{21}$

19) $1\frac{5}{3} + 7\frac{2}{6} = = 10\frac{0}{1}$

20) $2\frac{7}{5} + 5\frac{1}{6} = = 8\frac{17}{30}$

21) $2\frac{5}{4} + 5\frac{4}{1} = = 12\frac{1}{4}$

22) $2\frac{9}{3} + 6\frac{2}{2} = = 12\frac{0}{1}$

✏️ **Solve.**

1) $7\frac{1}{1} - 4\frac{5}{6} =$

2) $4\frac{6}{3} - 2\frac{2}{7} =$

3) $3\frac{8}{8} - 1\frac{4}{9} =$

4) $7\frac{7}{6} - 5\frac{3}{7} =$

5) $6\frac{5}{8} - 1\frac{3}{5} =$

6) $6\frac{4}{2} - 1\frac{2}{4} =$

7) $8\frac{5}{6} - 5\frac{1}{4} =$

8) $5\frac{6}{4} - 2\frac{5}{5} =$

9) $5\frac{6}{7} - 2\frac{2}{8} =$

10) $6\frac{4}{4} - 1\frac{4}{7} =$

11) $5\frac{6}{1} - 4\frac{5}{3} =$

12) $10\frac{2}{1} - 4\frac{5}{4} =$

13) $6\frac{7}{7} - 2\frac{4}{5} =$

14) $5\frac{3}{1} - 1\frac{1}{2} =$

15) $8\frac{9}{5} - 6\frac{3}{2} =$

16) $5\frac{7}{6} - 2\frac{2}{5} =$

17) $4\frac{6}{10} - 1\frac{1}{10} =$

18) $10\frac{9}{1} - 2\frac{5}{8} =$

19) $8\frac{5}{1} - 1\frac{6}{6} =$

20) $6\frac{6}{1} - 5\frac{2}{4} =$

21) $5\frac{1}{1} - 2\frac{1}{7} =$

22) $7\frac{2}{7} - 1\frac{2}{8} =$

✏️ **Solve.**

1) $7\frac{1}{1} - 4\frac{5}{6} = 3\frac{1}{6}$

2) $4\frac{6}{3} - 2\frac{2}{7} = 3\frac{5}{7}$

3) $3\frac{8}{8} - 1\frac{4}{9} = 2\frac{5}{9}$

4) $7\frac{7}{6} - 5\frac{3}{7} = 2\frac{31}{42}$

5) $6\frac{5}{8} - 1\frac{3}{5} = 5\frac{1}{40}$

6) $6\frac{4}{2} - 1\frac{2}{4} = 6\frac{1}{2}$

7) $8\frac{5}{6} - 5\frac{1}{4} = 3\frac{7}{12}$

8) $5\frac{6}{4} - 2\frac{5}{5} = 3\frac{1}{2}$

9) $5\frac{6}{7} - 2\frac{2}{8} = 3\frac{17}{28}$

10) $6\frac{4}{4} - 1\frac{4}{7} = 5\frac{3}{7}$

11) $5\frac{6}{1} - 4\frac{5}{3} = 5\frac{1}{3}$

12) $10\frac{2}{1} - 4\frac{5}{4} = 6\frac{3}{4}$

13) $6\frac{7}{7} - 2\frac{4}{5} = 4\frac{1}{5}$

14) $5\frac{3}{1} - 1\frac{1}{2} = 6\frac{1}{2}$

15) $8\frac{9}{5} - 6\frac{3}{2} = 2\frac{3}{10}$

16) $5\frac{7}{6} - 2\frac{2}{5} = 3\frac{23}{30}$

17) $4\frac{6}{10} - 1\frac{1}{10} = 3\frac{1}{2}$

18) $10\frac{9}{1} - 2\frac{5}{8} = 16\frac{3}{8}$

19) $8\frac{5}{1} - 1\frac{6}{6} = 11\frac{0}{1}$

20) $6\frac{6}{1} - 5\frac{2}{4} = 6\frac{1}{2}$

21) $5\frac{1}{1} - 2\frac{1}{7} = 3\frac{6}{7}$

22) $7\frac{2}{7} - 1\frac{2}{8} = 6\frac{1}{28}$

16

testinar.com/t/?c=2

✎▷ **Calculate.**

1) $4\frac{2}{3} \times 3\frac{3}{9} =$

2) $6\frac{4}{5} \times 4\frac{1}{9} =$

3) $6\frac{6}{9} \times 4\frac{2}{9} =$

4) $2\frac{7}{1} \times 1\frac{4}{9} =$

5) $10\frac{3}{4} \times 8\frac{6}{10} =$

6) $4\frac{7}{3} \times 2\frac{4}{10} =$

7) $6\frac{7}{2} \times 3\frac{4}{6} =$

8) $8\frac{5}{1} \times 1\frac{6}{3} =$

9) $6\frac{5}{1} \times 3\frac{2}{6} =$

10) $6\frac{7}{9} \times 2\frac{2}{6} =$

11) $7\frac{7}{8} \times 2\frac{3}{5} =$

12) $5\frac{2}{1} \times 4\frac{5}{3} =$

13) $3\frac{3}{1} \times 1\frac{7}{4} =$

14) $5\frac{6}{3} \times 4\frac{9}{5} =$

15) $4\frac{4}{3} \times 1\frac{6}{9} =$

16) $8\frac{5}{4} \times 2\frac{5}{8} =$

17) $7\frac{7}{5} \times 3\frac{1}{5} =$

18) $3\frac{6}{3} \times 1\frac{1}{3} =$

19) $2\frac{6}{4} \times 1\frac{3}{7} =$

20) $5\frac{9}{4} \times 4\frac{1}{2} =$

21) $8\frac{4}{1} \times 2\frac{1}{6} =$

22) $8\frac{4}{2} \times 4\frac{2}{5} =$

Calculate.

1) $4\frac{2}{3} \times 3\frac{3}{9} = 15\frac{5}{9}$

2) $6\frac{4}{5} \times 4\frac{1}{9} = 27\frac{43}{45}$

3) $6\frac{6}{9} \times 4\frac{2}{9} = 28\frac{4}{27}$

4) $2\frac{7}{1} \times 1\frac{4}{9} = 13$

5) $10\frac{3}{4} \times 8\frac{6}{10} = 92\frac{9}{20}$

6) $4\frac{7}{3} \times 2\frac{4}{10} = 15\frac{1}{5}$

7) $6\frac{7}{2} \times 3\frac{4}{6} = 34\frac{5}{6}$

8) $8\frac{5}{1} \times 1\frac{6}{3} = 39$

9) $6\frac{5}{1} \times 3\frac{2}{6} = 36\frac{2}{3}$

10) $6\frac{7}{9} \times 2\frac{2}{6} = 15\frac{22}{27}$

11) $7\frac{7}{8} \times 2\frac{3}{5} = 20\frac{19}{40}$

12) $5\frac{2}{1} \times 4\frac{5}{3} = 39\frac{2}{3}$

13) $3\frac{3}{1} \times 1\frac{7}{4} = 16\frac{1}{2}$

14) $5\frac{6}{3} \times 4\frac{9}{5} = 40\frac{3}{5}$

15) $4\frac{4}{3} \times 1\frac{6}{9} = 8\frac{8}{9}$

16) $8\frac{5}{4} \times 2\frac{5}{8} = 24\frac{9}{32}$

17) $7\frac{7}{5} \times 3\frac{1}{5} = 26\frac{22}{25}$

18) $3\frac{6}{3} \times 1\frac{1}{3} = 6\frac{2}{3}$

19) $2\frac{6}{4} \times 1\frac{3}{7} = 5$

20) $5\frac{9}{4} \times 4\frac{1}{2} = 32\frac{5}{8}$

21) $8\frac{4}{1} \times 2\frac{1}{6} = 26$

22) $8\frac{4}{2} \times 4\frac{2}{5} = 44$

testinar.com/t/?c=2

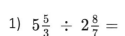 **Solve.**

1) $5\frac{5}{3} \div 2\frac{8}{7} =$

2) $8\frac{1}{5} \div 6\frac{1}{6} =$

3) $10\frac{4}{2} \div 3\frac{5}{10} =$

4) $5\frac{8}{4} \div 2\frac{5}{9} =$

5) $6\frac{3}{2} \div 1\frac{1}{3} =$

6) $7\frac{2}{9} \div 3\frac{1}{5} =$

7) $8\frac{9}{10} \div 4\frac{4}{5} =$

8) $7\frac{4}{5} \div 3\frac{1}{4} =$

9) $6\frac{6}{3} \div 1\frac{7}{6} =$

10) $6\frac{2}{1} \div 5\frac{4}{9} =$

11) $8\frac{4}{5} \div 2\frac{3}{5} =$

12) $7\frac{7}{2} \div 4\frac{3}{1} =$

13) $8\frac{8}{5} \div 1\frac{5}{7} =$

14) $8\frac{4}{6} \div 6\frac{2}{6} =$

15) $8\frac{9}{5} \div 3\frac{2}{7} =$

16) $10\frac{2}{5} \div 5\frac{2}{10} =$

17) $8\frac{9}{4} \div 1\frac{1}{3} =$

18) $7\frac{7}{4} \div 6\frac{6}{9} =$

19) $8\frac{2}{4} \div 1\frac{1}{9} =$

20) $8\frac{4}{3} \div 5\frac{3}{7} =$

21) $8\frac{7}{2} \div 6\frac{6}{5} =$

22) $8\frac{7}{2} \div 7\frac{6}{4} =$

✏️ **Solve.**

1) $5\frac{5}{3} \div 2\frac{8}{7} = 2\frac{4}{33}$

2) $8\frac{1}{5} \div 6\frac{1}{6} = 1\frac{61}{185}$

3) $10\frac{4}{2} \div 3\frac{5}{10} = 3\frac{3}{7}$

4) $5\frac{8}{4} \div 2\frac{5}{9} = 2\frac{17}{23}$

5) $6\frac{3}{2} \div 1\frac{1}{3} = 5\frac{5}{8}$

6) $7\frac{2}{9} \div 3\frac{1}{5} = 2\frac{37}{144}$

7) $8\frac{9}{10} \div 4\frac{4}{5} = 1\frac{41}{48}$

8) $7\frac{4}{5} \div 3\frac{1}{4} = 2\frac{2}{5}$

9) $6\frac{6}{3} \div 1\frac{7}{6} = 3\frac{9}{13}$

10) $6\frac{2}{1} \div 5\frac{4}{9} = 1\frac{23}{49}$

11) $8\frac{4}{5} \div 2\frac{3}{5} = 3\frac{5}{13}$

12) $7\frac{7}{2} \div 4\frac{3}{1} = 1\frac{1}{2}$

13) $8\frac{8}{5} \div 1\frac{5}{7} = 5\frac{3}{5}$

14) $8\frac{4}{6} \div 6\frac{2}{6} = 1\frac{7}{19}$

15) $8\frac{9}{5} \div 3\frac{2}{7} = 2\frac{113}{115}$

16) $10\frac{2}{5} \div 5\frac{2}{10} = 2$

17) $8\frac{9}{4} \div 1\frac{1}{3} = 7\frac{11}{16}$

18) $7\frac{7}{4} \div 6\frac{6}{9} = 1\frac{5}{16}$

19) $8\frac{2}{4} \div 1\frac{1}{9} = 7\frac{13}{20}$

20) $8\frac{4}{3} \div 5\frac{3}{7} = 1\frac{41}{57}$

21) $8\frac{7}{2} \div 6\frac{6}{5} = 1\frac{43}{72}$

22) $8\frac{7}{2} \div 7\frac{6}{4} = 1\frac{6}{17}$

▷ Use > = <.

1) 22.09 □ 94.88

2) 13.35 □ 67.76

3) 66.94 □ 66.94

4) 25.19 □ 22.71

5) 96.27 □ 96.27

6) 67.83 □ 19.93

7) 29.16 □ 0.43

8) 379.2 □ 37.92

9) 815.7 □ 81.57

10) 3.12 □ 3.12

11) 513.5 □ 51.35

12) 819.7 □ 81.97

13) 277.5 □ 27.75

14) 65.5 □ 42.81

15) 79.06 □ 39.16

16) 61.72 □ 6.172

17) 438.1 □ 43.81

18) 40.25 □ 40.25

19) 101.37 □ 93.83

20) 94.42 □ 34.66

21) 18.8 □ 1.88

22) 23.24 □ 96.95

 Use > = <.

1) 22.09 $<$ 94.88

2) 13.35 $<$ 67.76

3) 66.94 $=$ 66.94

4) 25.19 $>$ 22.71

5) 96.27 $=$ 96.27

6) 67.83 $>$ 19.93

7) 29.16 $>$ 0.43

8) 379.2 $>$ 37.92

9) 815.7 $>$ 81.57

10) 3.12 $=$ 3.12

11) 513.5 $>$ 51.35

12) 819.7 $>$ 81.97

13) 277.5 $>$ 27.75

14) 65.5 $>$ 42.81

15) 79.06 $>$ 39.16

16) 61.72 $>$ 6.172

17) 438.1 $>$ 43.81

18) 40.25 $=$ 40.25

19) 101.37 $>$ 93.83

20) 94.42 $>$ 34.66

21) 18.8 $>$ 1.88

22) 23.24 $<$ 96.95

Rounding Decimals

✏ **Round each decimal number to the nearest place indicated.**

1) 16.2̲43

2) 10.28̲5

3) 10̲.590

4) 14.6̲43

5) 15̲.637

6) 15.9̲11

7) 17.33̲1

8) 13.67̲6

9) 13̲.496

✏ **Round each decimal to the nearest whole number.**

1) 5.351

2) 21.188

3) 23.633

4) 26.586

5) 31.491

6) 11.106

7) 19.209

8) 29.205

9) 8.601

✏ **Round each decimal to the nearest tenth.**

1) 68.347

2) 41.266

3) 45.782

4) 55.532

5) 65.674

6) 61.333

7) 63.801

8) 64.394

9) 49.501

✏ **Round each decimal to the nearest hundredth.**

1) 51.392

2) 63.708

3) 64.951

4) 66.152

5) 60.286

6) 50.131

7) 46.991

8) 69.362

9) 68.386

✏️▶ **Round each decimal number to the nearest place indicated.**

1) 16.2̲43 ⇒ 16.2

2) 10.28̲5 ⇒ 10.28

3) 1̲0.590 ⇒ 11

4) 14.6̲43 ⇒ 14.6

5) 15̲.637 ⇒ 16

6) 15.9̲11 ⇒ 15.9

7) 17.33̲1 ⇒ 17.33

8) 13.67̲6 ⇒ 13.68

9) 1̲3.496 ⇒ 13

✏️▶ **Round each decimal to the nearest whole number.**

1) 5.351 ⇒ 5

2) 21.188 ⇒ 21

3) 23.633 ⇒ 24

4) 26.586 ⇒ 27

5) 31.491 ⇒ 31

6) 11.106 ⇒ 11

7) 19.209 ⇒ 19

8) 29.205 ⇒ 29

9) 8.601 ⇒ 9

✏️▶ **Round each decimal to the nearest tenth.**

1) 68.347 ⇒ 68.3

2) 41.266 ⇒ 41.3

3) 45.782 ⇒ 45.8

4) 55.532 ⇒ 55.5

5) 65.674 ⇒ 65.7

6) 61.333 ⇒ 61.3

7) 63.801 ⇒ 63.8

8) 64.394 ⇒ 64.4

9) 49.501 ⇒ 49.5

✏️▶ **Round each decimal to the nearest hundredth.**

1) 51.392 ⇒ 51.39

2) 63.708 ⇒ 63.71

3) 64.951 ⇒ 64.95

4) 66.152 ⇒ 66.15

5) 60.286 ⇒ 60.29

6) 50.131 ⇒ 50.13

7) 46.991 ⇒ 46.99

8) 69.362 ⇒ 69.36

9) 68.386 ⇒ 68.39

 Solve.

1) $\begin{array}{r} 67.8 \\ \times\ 34.1 \\ \hline \end{array}$

2) $\begin{array}{r} 76.6 \\ \times\ 24.2 \\ \hline \end{array}$

3) $\begin{array}{r} 27.8 \\ \times\ 17.3 \\ \hline \end{array}$

4) $\begin{array}{r} 71.6 \\ \times\ 15.2 \\ \hline \end{array}$

5) $\begin{array}{r} 45.4 \\ \times\ 11.7 \\ \hline \end{array}$

6) $\begin{array}{r} 88.1 \\ \times\ 32.6 \\ \hline \end{array}$

7) $\begin{array}{r} 81.3 \\ \times\ 28.2 \\ \hline \end{array}$

8) $\begin{array}{r} 22.4 \\ \times\ 13.5 \\ \hline \end{array}$

9) $\begin{array}{r} 61.2 \\ \times\ 23.8 \\ \hline \end{array}$

10) $\begin{array}{r} 31.2 \\ \times\ 14.6 \\ \hline \end{array}$

11) $\begin{array}{r} 22.1 \\ \times\ 16.1 \\ \hline \end{array}$

12) $\begin{array}{r} 36.5 \\ \times\ 17.8 \\ \hline \end{array}$

Solve.

1) $71.4 \div 58.4$

2) $43.6 \div 34.2$

3) $26.6 \div 6.2$

4) $45.8 \div 27.4$

5) $72.6 \div 18.7$

6) $13.3 \div 2.4$

7) $56.1 \div 24.3$

8) $38.7 \div 31.1$

✏️ **Solve.**

1) $\begin{array}{r} 67.8 \\ \times\ 34.1 \\ \hline 2311.98 \end{array}$

2) $\begin{array}{r} 76.6 \\ \times\ 24.2 \\ \hline 1853.72 \end{array}$

3) $\begin{array}{r} 27.8 \\ \times\ 17.3 \\ \hline 480.94 \end{array}$

4) $\begin{array}{r} 71.6 \\ \times\ 15.2 \\ \hline 1088.32 \end{array}$

5) $\begin{array}{r} 45.4 \\ \times\ 11.7 \\ \hline 531.18 \end{array}$

6) $\begin{array}{r} 88.1 \\ \times\ 32.6 \\ \hline 2872.06 \end{array}$

7) $\begin{array}{r} 81.3 \\ \times\ 28.2 \\ \hline 2292.66 \end{array}$

8) $\begin{array}{r} 22.4 \\ \times\ 13.5 \\ \hline 302.4 \end{array}$

9) $\begin{array}{r} 61.2 \\ \times\ 23.8 \\ \hline 1456.56 \end{array}$

10) $\begin{array}{r} 31.2 \\ \times\ 14.6 \\ \hline 455.52 \end{array}$

11) $\begin{array}{r} 22.1 \\ \times\ 16.1 \\ \hline 355.81 \end{array}$

12) $\begin{array}{r} 36.5 \\ \times\ 17.8 \\ \hline 649.7 \end{array}$

✏️ **Solve.**

1) $71.4 \div 58.4 = 1.2226...$

2) $43.6 \div 34.2 = 1.2749...$

3) $26.6 \div 6.2 = 4.2903...$

4) $45.8 \div 27.4 = 1.6715...$

5) $72.6 \div 18.7 = 3.8824...$

6) $13.3 \div 2.4 = 5.5417...$

7) $56.1 \div 24.3 = 2.3086...$

8) $38.7 \div 31.1 = 1.2444...$

testinar.com/t/?c=2

✎ **Convert fractions to decimals.**

1) $\frac{3}{10} =$

2) $\frac{5}{3} =$

3) $\frac{15}{1000} =$

4) $\frac{4}{7} =$

5) $\frac{3}{19} =$

6) $\frac{6}{3} =$

7) $\frac{4}{2} =$

8) $\frac{6}{10} =$

9) $\frac{14}{100} =$

10) $\frac{5}{2} =$

11) $\frac{8}{14} =$

12) $\frac{10}{1000} =$

13) $\frac{17}{10} =$

14) $\frac{20}{1000} =$

15) $\frac{3}{6} =$

✎ **Convert decimals to fractions.**

1) $0.34 =$

2) $0.38 =$

3) $0.81 =$

4) $0.25 =$

5) $0.45 =$

6) $0.13 =$

7) $0.14 =$

8) $0.21 =$

9) $0.44 =$

10) $0.31 =$

11) $0.12 =$

12) $0.47 =$

13) $0.43 =$

14) $0.35 =$

15) $0.17 =$

✏️ **Convert fractions to decimals.**

1) $\frac{3}{10} = 0.3$

2) $\frac{5}{3} = 1.667...$

3) $\frac{15}{1000} = 0.015$

4) $\frac{4}{7} = 0.571...$

5) $\frac{3}{19} = 0.158...$

6) $\frac{6}{3} = 2$

7) $\frac{4}{2} = 2$

8) $\frac{6}{10} = 0.6$

9) $\frac{14}{100} = 0.14$

10) $\frac{5}{2} = 2.5$

11) $\frac{8}{14} = 0.571...$

12) $\frac{10}{1000} = 0.01$

13) $\frac{17}{10} = 1.7$

14) $\frac{20}{1000} = 0.02$

15) $\frac{3}{6} = 0.5$

✏️ **Convert decimals to fractions.**

1) $0.34 = \frac{17}{50}$

2) $0.38 = \frac{19}{50}$

3) $0.81 = \frac{81}{100}$

4) $0.25 = \frac{1}{4}$

5) $0.45 = \frac{9}{20}$

6) $0.13 = \frac{13}{100}$

7) $0.14 = \frac{7}{50}$

8) $0.21 = \frac{21}{100}$

9) $0.44 = \frac{11}{25}$

10) $0.31 = \frac{31}{100}$

11) $0.12 = \frac{3}{25}$

12) $0.47 = \frac{47}{100}$

13) $0.43 = \frac{43}{100}$

14) $0.35 = \frac{7}{20}$

15) $0.17 = \frac{17}{100}$

✏️ **Solve.**

1) $8 + (-23) - (-5) =$

2) $(-43) + 13 - (-9) =$

3) $(-47) + (-12) =$

4) $(-15) + (-13) + (-25) =$

5) $(-35) + (-24) =$

6) $24 + (-10) - (-27) =$

7) $(-7) + (-15) - (-7) =$

8) $21 + (-16) + (-22) =$

9) $(-2) + 7 + (-30) =$

10) $33 + (-11) =$

11) $7 + (-27) + (-26) =$

12) $(-46) + (-23) =$

13) $39 + 18 + (-14) =$

14) $10 + 6 + (-18) =$

15) $49 + 19 + (-14) =$

16) $(-1) + (-15) =$

17) $20 + 24 + (-28) =$

18) $(-33) + 24 - (-14) =$

19) $(-49) + (-6) + (-16) =$

20) $39 + (-8) - (-12) =$

21) $28 + (-27) - (-27) =$

22) $18 + (-8) + (-13) =$

✏️ **Solve.**

1) $8 + (-23) - (-5) = -10$

2) $(-43) + 13 - (-9) = -21$

3) $(-47) + (-12) = -59$

4) $(-15) + (-13) + (-25) = -53$

5) $(-35) + (-24) = -59$

6) $24 + (-10) - (-27) = 41$

7) $(-7) + (-15) - (-7) = -15$

8) $21 + (-16) + (-22) = -17$

9) $(-2) + 7 + (-30) = -25$

10) $33 + (-11) = 22$

11) $7 + (-27) + (-26) = -46$

12) $(-46) + (-23) = -69$

13) $39 + 18 + (-14) = 43$

14) $10 + 6 + (-18) = -2$

15) $49 + 19 + (-14) = 54$

16) $(-1) + (-15) = -16$

17) $20 + 24 + (-28) = 16$

18) $(-33) + 24 - (-14) = 5$

19) $(-49) + (-6) + (-16) = -71$

20) $39 + (-8) - (-12) = 43$

21) $28 + (-27) - (-27) = 28$

22) $18 + (-8) + (-13) = -3$

▱▶ **Get the result.**

testinar.com/t/?c=3

1) $0 \div 0 =$

2) $9 \times 2 \times (-4) =$

3) $3 \times 1 \times (-4) =$

4) $(-8) \div (-4) =$

5) $9 \times 7 \times (-9) =$

6) $2 \times 1 \times (-7) =$

7) $(-6) \times 7 \times (-6) =$

8) $4 \times (-4) =$

9) $4 \times 4 =$

10) $(-4) \times (-5) =$

11) $5 \times (-5) =$

12) $10 \div 5 =$

13) $(-5) \times 4 \times (-9) =$

14) $1 \times (-9) \times (-10) =$

15) $(-9) \times 4 \times (-3) =$

16) $(-4) \times 4 =$

17) $(-24) \div 8 =$

18) $(-8) \times (-6) \times (-7) =$

19) $6 \times (-9) \times (-7) =$

20) $0 \times (-2) \times (-6) =$

21) $2 \times 1 =$

22) $(-1) \times 3 \times (-9) =$

Answers of Multiplying and Dividing Integers

Get the result.

1) $0 \div 0 = -4$

2) $9 \times 2 \times (-4) = -72$

3) $3 \times 1 \times (-4) = -12$

4) $(-8) \div (-4) = 2$

5) $9 \times 7 \times (-9) = -567$

6) $2 \times 1 \times (-7) = -14$

7) $(-6) \times 7 \times (-6) = 252$

8) $4 \times (-4) = -16$

9) $4 \times 4 = 16$

10) $(-4) \times (-5) = 20$

11) $5 \times (-5) = -25$

12) $10 \div 5 = 2$

13) $(-5) \times 4 \times (-9) = 180$

14) $1 \times (-9) \times (-10) = 90$

15) $(-9) \times 4 \times (-3) = 108$

16) $(-4) \times 4 = -16$

17) $(-24) \div 8 = -3$

18) $(-8) \times (-6) \times (-7) = -336$

19) $6 \times (-9) \times (-7) = 378$

20) $0 \times (-2) \times (-6) = 0$

21) $2 \times 1 = 2$

22) $(-1) \times 3 \times (-9) = 27$

▱> **Evaluate each expression.**

1) $(-9) \times 5 + 11 \times 4 =$

2) $6 \times 6 - 15 =$

3) $6 \times 4 - 12 =$

4) $49 \div 7 + 4 =$

5) $-24 \div 6 + 6 =$

6) $(-8) \times 1 + 5 =$

7) $64 \div 8 + 2 =$

8) $3 \times (-8) + 5 =$

9) $-32 \div 8 + 6 =$

10) $(-7) \times (-6) - 19 =$

11) $(-4) \times 2 + 2 =$

12) $(-8) \times (-2) - 10 =$

13) $8 \times (-8) - 13 =$

14) $9 \times 4 - 16 =$

15) $6 \times 4 - 20 =$

16) $2 \times 7 + 11 \times 3 =$

17) $0 \div 8 + 5 =$

18) $(-6) \times (-4) - 3 =$

19) $(-7) \times (-5) - 21 =$

20) $(-6) \times 9 + 18 =$

21) $-6 \div 6 + 7 =$

22) $(-3) \times 7 + 6 \times 6 =$

Answers of Order of Operations

✏️ **Evaluate each expression.**

1) $(-9) \times 5 + 11 \times 4 = -1$

2) $6 \times 6 - 15 = 21$

3) $6 \times 4 - 12 = 12$

4) $49 \div 7 + 4 = 11$

5) $-24 \div 6 + 6 = 2$

6) $(-8) \times 1 + 5 = -3$

7) $64 \div 8 + 2 = 10$

8) $3 \times (-8) + 5 = -19$

9) $-32 \div 8 + 6 = 2$

10) $(-7) \times (-6) - 19 = 23$

11) $(-4) \times 2 + 2 = -6$

12) $(-8) \times (-2) - 10 = 6$

13) $8 \times (-8) - 13 = -77$

14) $9 \times 4 - 16 = 20$

15) $6 \times 4 - 20 = 4$

16) $2 \times 7 + 11 \times 3 = 47$

17) $0 \div 8 + 5 = 5$

18) $(-6) \times (-4) - 3 = 21$

19) $(-7) \times (-5) - 21 = 14$

20) $(-6) \times 9 + 18 = -36$

21) $-6 \div 6 + 7 = 6$

22) $(-3) \times 7 + 6 \times 6 = 15$

testinar.com/t/?c=3

 Solve.

1) $|14| =$

2) $|15| =$

3) $|16| =$

4) $|2| =$

5) $|-11| =$

6) $|-1| =$

7) $|-12| =$

8) $|-16| =$

9) $|-2| =$

10) $|20| =$

11) $|-18| =$

12) $|-4| =$

13) $|11| =$

14) $|-9| =$

15) $|18| =$

16) $|-8| =$

17) $|9| =$

18) $|10| =$

 Evaluate.

1) $|-8| + |2| =$

2) $|-5| + |-8| =$

3) $|-11| + |4| =$

4) $6 + |3| =$

5) $-15 + |1| =$

6) $|-13| + |3| =$

7) $17 + |-7| =$

8) $-18 + |6| =$

9) $|17| + |-1| =$

10) $|7| + |-2| =$

11) $|-3| + |6| =$

12) $-2 + |-10| =$

13) $14 + |8| =$

14) $20 + |-3| =$

15) $11 + |-8| =$

35

Solve.

1) $|14| = 14$

2) $|15| = 15$

3) $|16| = 16$

4) $|2| = 2$

5) $|-11| = 11$

6) $|-1| = 1$

7) $|-12| = 12$

8) $|-16| = 16$

9) $|-2| = 2$

10) $|20| = 20$

11) $|-18| = 18$

12) $|-4| = 4$

13) $|11| = 11$

14) $|-9| = 9$

15) $|18| = 18$

16) $|-8| = 8$

17) $|9| = 9$

18) $|10| = 10$

Evaluate.

1) $|-8| + |2| = 10$

2) $|-5| + |-8| = 13$

3) $|-11| + |4| = 15$

4) $6 + |3| = 9$

5) $-15 + |1| = -14$

6) $|-13| + |3| = 16$

7) $17 + |-7| = 24$

8) $-18 + |6| = -12$

9) $|17| + |-1| = 18$

10) $|7| + |-2| = 9$

11) $|-3| + |6| = 9$

12) $-2 + |-10| = 8$

13) $14 + |8| = 22$

14) $20 + |-3| = 23$

15) $11 + |-8| = 19$

✏️ **Express each ratio as a rate and unit rate.**

1) 126.00 dollars for 6 books

2) 55.00 dollars for 5 books

3) 117 inches of snow in 39 hours

4) 145.00 dollars for 5 books

5) 39 inches of snow in 13 hours

6) 112 inches of snow in 28 hours

7) 51.00 dollars for 3 books

8) 105.00 dollars for 3 books

9) 69 miles on 3 gallons of gas

10) 150 miles on 6 gallons of gas

✏️ **Express each ratio as a fraction in the simplest form.**

1) 40 miles out of 50 miles

2) 5 miles out of 25 miles

3) 36 miles out of 51 miles

4) 15 miles out of 33 miles

5) 24 miles out of 28 miles

6) 35 miles out of 45 miles

7) 55 miles out of 60 miles

8) 6 cakes out of 27 cakes

9) 17 dimes out of 51 coins

10) 25 cakes out of 35 cakes

> **Express each ratio as a rate and unit rate.**

1) 126.00 dollars for 6 books ⇒ 21.00 dollars per book

2) 55.00 dollars for 5 books ⇒ 11.00 dollars per book

3) 117 inches of snow in 39 hours ⇒ 3 inches of snow per hour

4) 145.00 dollars for 5 books ⇒ 29.00 dollars per book

5) 39 inches of snow in 13 hours ⇒ 3 inches of snow per hour

6) 112 inches of snow in 28 hours ⇒ 4 inches of snow per hour

7) 51.00 dollars for 3 books ⇒ 17.00 dollars per book

8) 105.00 dollars for 3 books ⇒ 35.00 dollars per book

9) 69 miles on 3 gallons of gas ⇒ 23 miles per gallon

10) 150 miles on 6 gallons of gas ⇒ 25 miles per gallon

> **Express each ratio as a fraction in the simplest form.**

1) 40 miles out of 50 miles ⇒ $\frac{4}{5}$

2) 5 miles out of 25 miles ⇒ $\frac{1}{5}$

3) 36 miles out of 51 miles ⇒ $\frac{12}{17}$

4) 15 miles out of 33 miles ⇒ $\frac{5}{11}$

5) 24 miles out of 28 miles ⇒ $\frac{6}{7}$

6) 35 miles out of 45 miles ⇒ $\frac{7}{9}$

7) 55 miles out of 60 miles ⇒ $\frac{11}{12}$

8) 6 cakes out of 27 cakes ⇒ $\frac{2}{9}$

9) 17 dimes out of 51 coins ⇒ $\frac{1}{3}$

10) 25 cakes out of 35 cakes ⇒ $\frac{5}{7}$

Reduce each ratio.

1) $6 : 15 =$

2) $8 : 52 =$

3) $57 : 84 =$

4) $14 : 21 =$

5) $6 : 30 =$

6) $57 : 87 =$

7) $35 : 50 =$

8) $3 : 69 =$

9) $14 : 77 =$

10) $33 : 48 =$

11) $69 : 75 =$

12) $51 : 60 =$

13) $12 : 39 =$

14) $39 : 90 =$

15) $52 : 56 =$

Write each ratio as a fraction in simplest form.

1) $3 : 12 =$

2) $32 : 36 =$

3) $32 : 76 =$

4) $12 : 21 =$

5) $7 : 42 =$

6) $16 : 32 =$

7) $9 : 87 =$

8) $18 : 90 =$

9) $32 : 72 =$

10) $40 : 48 =$

11) $55 : 65 =$

12) $57 : 81 =$

13) $30 : 54 =$

14) $54 : 69 =$

15) $35 : 63 =$

39

✏️ **Reduce each ratio.**

1) $6 : 15 = 2 : 5$

2) $8 : 52 = 2 : 13$

3) $57 : 84 = 19 : 28$

4) $14 : 21 = 2 : 3$

5) $6 : 30 = 1 : 5$

6) $57 : 87 = 19 : 29$

7) $35 : 50 = 7 : 10$

8) $3 : 69 = 1 : 23$

9) $14 : 77 = 2 : 11$

10) $33 : 48 = 11 : 16$

11) $69 : 75 = 23 : 25$

12) $51 : 60 = 17 : 20$

13) $12 : 39 = 4 : 13$

14) $39 : 90 = 13 : 30$

15) $52 : 56 = 13 : 14$

✏️ **Write each ratio as a fraction in simplest form.**

1) $3 : 12 = \frac{1}{4}$

2) $32 : 36 = \frac{8}{9}$

3) $32 : 76 = \frac{8}{19}$

4) $12 : 21 = \frac{4}{7}$

5) $7 : 42 = \frac{1}{6}$

6) $16 : 32 = \frac{1}{2}$

7) $9 : 87 = \frac{3}{29}$

8) $18 : 90 = \frac{1}{5}$

9) $32 : 72 = \frac{4}{9}$

10) $40 : 48 = \frac{5}{6}$

11) $55 : 65 = \frac{11}{13}$

12) $57 : 81 = \frac{19}{27}$

13) $30 : 54 = \frac{5}{9}$

14) $54 : 69 = \frac{18}{23}$

15) $35 : 63 = \frac{5}{9}$

Each pair of figures is similar. Find the missing side.

1) $x =$

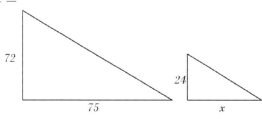

2) $x =$

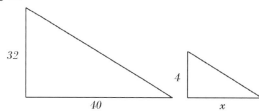

3) $x =$

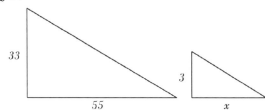

4) $x =$

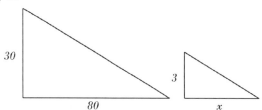

5) $x =$

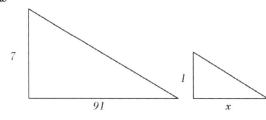

6) $x =$

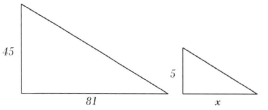

7) $x =$

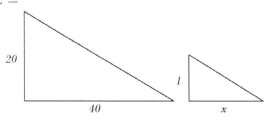

8) $x =$

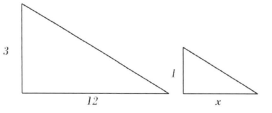

✏️▶ **Each pair of figures is similar. Find the missing side.**

1) $x = 25$

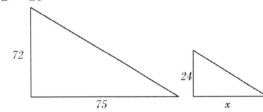

2) $x = 5$

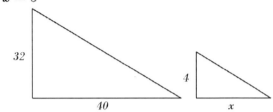

3) $x = 5$

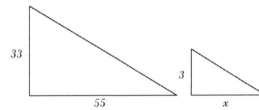

4) $x = 8$

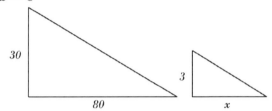

5) $x = 13$

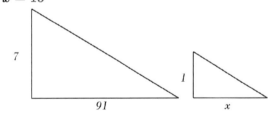

6) $x = 9$

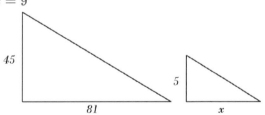

7) $x = 2$

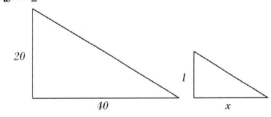

8) $x = 4$

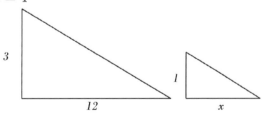

testinar.com/t/?c=4

✏️ **Fill in the blanks; solve each proportion.**

1) $16 : 88 = \underline{} : 11$

2) $25 : 30 = \underline{} : 6$

3) $6 : 81 = \underline{} : 27$

4) $15 : 75 = 1 : \underline{}$

5) $56 : 76 = \underline{} : 19$

6) $10 : 35 = \underline{} : 7$

7) $22 : 55 = 2 : \underline{}$

8) $8 : 16 = \underline{} : 2$

9) $6 : 21 = \underline{} : 7$

10) $12 : 28 = \underline{} : 7$

11) $15 : 87 = \underline{} : 29$

12) $13 : 26 = 1 : \underline{}$

13) $21 : 60 = 7 : \underline{}$

14) $28 : 32 = \underline{} : 8$

15) $24 : 27 = \underline{} : 9$

16) $70 : 80 = 7 : \underline{}$

17) $6 : 93 = 2 : \underline{}$

18) $15 : 51 = 5 : \underline{}$

19) $15 : 20 = \underline{} : 4$

20) $16 : 24 = \underline{} : 3$

21) $24 : 39 = \underline{} : 13$

22) $49 : 56 = 7 : \underline{}$

23) $48 : 76 = 12 : \underline{}$

24) $3 : 63 = \underline{} : 21$

25) $48 : 92 = 12 : \underline{}$

26) $76 : 80 = \underline{} : 20$

27) $75 : 84 = \underline{} : 28$

28) $63 : 77 = \underline{} : 11$

29) $20 : 65 = \underline{} : 13$

30) $20 : 36 = \underline{} : 9$

31) $21 : 57 = 7 : \underline{}$

32) $6 : 33 = 2 : \underline{}$

33) $85 : 90 = 17 : \underline{}$

✏️ **Fill in the blanks; solve each proportion.**

1) $16 : 88 = 2 : 11$

2) $25 : 30 = 5 : 6$

3) $6 : 81 = 2 : 27$

4) $15 : 75 = 1 : 5$

5) $56 : 76 = 14 : 19$

6) $10 : 35 = 2 : 7$

7) $22 : 55 = 2 : 5$

8) $8 : 16 = 1 : 2$

9) $6 : 21 = 2 : 7$

10) $12 : 28 = 3 : 7$

11) $15 : 87 = 5 : 29$

12) $13 : 26 = 1 : 2$

13) $21 : 60 = 7 : 20$

14) $28 : 32 = 7 : 8$

15) $24 : 27 = 8 : 9$

16) $70 : 80 = 7 : 8$

17) $6 : 93 = 2 : 31$

18) $15 : 51 = 5 : 17$

19) $15 : 20 = 3 : 4$

20) $16 : 24 = 2 : 3$

21) $24 : 39 = 8 : 13$

22) $49 : 56 = 7 : 8$

23) $48 : 76 = 12 : 19$

24) $3 : 63 = 1 : 21$

25) $48 : 92 = 12 : 23$

26) $76 : 80 = 19 : 20$

27) $75 : 84 = 25 : 28$

28) $63 : 77 = 9 : 11$

29) $20 : 65 = 4 : 13$

30) $20 : 36 = 5 : 9$

31) $21 : 57 = 7 : 19$

32) $6 : 33 = 2 : 11$

33) $85 : 90 = 17 : 18$

testinar.com/t/?c=5

✏️ **Calculate the percentages.**

1) 95% of $87 =$

2) 45% of $59 =$

3) 80% of $72 =$

4) 60% of $46 =$

5) 65% of $96 =$

6) 25% of $33 =$

7) 40% of $22 =$

8) 85% of $98 =$

9) 90% of $66 =$

10) 75% of $70 =$

✏️ **Solve.**

1) 51.1 is what percentage of 73?

2) 5.5 is what percentage of 22?

3) 68.25 is what percentage of 91?

4) 54.15 is what percentage of 57?

5) 16.8 is what percentage of 56?

6) 46.8 is what percentage of 72?

7) 27.3 is what percentage of 39?

8) 15.3 is what percentage of 34?

9) 9.45 is what percentage of 27?

10) 72.75 is what percentage of 97?

11) 37.95 is what percentage of 69?

12) 53.25 is what percentage of 71?

✏️ **Calculate the percentages.**

1) 95% of $87 = 82.65$

2) 45% of $59 = 26.55$

3) 80% of $72 = 57.6$

4) 60% of $46 = 27.6$

5) 65% of $96 = 62.4$

6) 25% of $33 = 8.25$

7) 40% of $22 = 8.8$

8) 85% of $98 = 83.3$

9) 90% of $66 = 59.4$

10) 75% of $70 = 52.5$

✏️ **Solve.**

1) 51.1 is what percentage of 73? 70%

2) 5.5 is what percentage of 22? 25%

3) 68.25 is what percentage of 91? 75%

4) 54.15 is what percentage of 57? 95%

5) 16.8 is what percentage of 56? 30%

6) 46.8 is what percentage of 72? 65%

7) 27.3 is what percentage of 39? 70%

8) 15.3 is what percentage of 34? 45%

9) 9.45 is what percentage of 27? 35%

10) 72.75 is what percentage of 97? 75%

11) 37.95 is what percentage of 69? 55%

12) 53.25 is what percentage of 71? 75%

✏️ **Converting fractions to decimals.**

1) $\frac{85}{100} =$

2) $\frac{30}{100} =$

3) $\frac{65}{100} =$

4) $\frac{45}{100} =$

5) $\frac{25}{100} =$

6) $\frac{50}{100} =$

7) $\frac{80}{100} =$

8) $\frac{15}{100} =$

9) $\frac{40}{100} =$

10) $\frac{90}{100} =$

✏️ **Write each decimal as a percent.**

1) $0.665 =$

2) $0.34 =$

3) $0.66 =$

4) $0.18 =$

5) $0.425 =$

6) $0.295 =$

7) $0.315 =$

8) $0.845 =$

9) $0.31 =$

10) $0.52 =$

11) $0.45 =$

12) $0.875 =$

▱➤ **Converting fractions to decimals.**

1) $\frac{85}{100} = 0.85$

2) $\frac{30}{100} = 0.3$

3) $\frac{65}{100} = 0.65$

4) $\frac{45}{100} = 0.45$

5) $\frac{25}{100} = 0.25$

6) $\frac{50}{100} = 0.5$

7) $\frac{80}{100} = 0.8$

8) $\frac{15}{100} = 0.15$

9) $\frac{40}{100} = 0.4$

10) $\frac{90}{100} = 0.9$

▱➤ **Write each decimal as a percent.**

1) $0.665 = 66.5\%$

2) $0.34 = 34\%$

3) $0.66 = 66\%$

4) $0.18 = 18\%$

5) $0.425 = 42.5\%$

6) $0.295 = 29.5\%$

7) $0.315 = 31.5\%$

8) $0.845 = 84.5\%$

9) $0.31 = 31\%$

10) $0.52 = 52\%$

11) $0.45 = 45\%$

12) $0.875 = 87.5\%$

Solve each problem.

1) 92 is 736% of what?

2) 58 is 174% of what?

3) What percent of 70 is 14.28?

4) What percent of 60 is 33.33?

5) What percent of 62 is 11.11?

6) 98 is 490% of what?

7) 54 is 378% of what?

8) 62 is 124% of what?

9) 78 is 624% of what?

10) What percent of 88 is 11.11?

11) 72 is 576% of what?

12) 88 is 792% of what?

13) 68 is 136% of what?

14) What percent of 54 is 20?

15) 84 is 588% of what?

16) What percent of 66 is 33.33?

17) 74 is 296% of what?

18) 60 is 600% of what?

19) What percent of 74 is 25?

20) What percent of 80 is 11.11?

21) What percent of 82 is 10?

22) 76 is 228% of what?

➡️ **Solve each problem.**

1) 92 is 736% of what? 12.5

2) 58 is 174% of what? 33.33

3) What percent of 70 is 14.28? 20.39%

4) What percent of 60 is 33.33? 55.55%

5) What percent of 62 is 11.11? 17.91%

6) 98 is 490% of what? 20

7) 54 is 378% of what? 14.28

8) 62 is 124% of what? 50

9) 78 is 624% of what? 12.5

10) What percent of 88 is 11.11? 12.62%

11) 72 is 576% of what? 12.5

12) 88 is 792% of what? 11.11

13) 68 is 136% of what? 50

14) What percent of 54 is 20? 37.03%

15) 84 is 588% of what? 14.28

16) What percent of 66 is 33.33? 50.5%

17) 74 is 296% of what? 25

18) 60 is 600% of what? 10

19) What percent of 74 is 25? 33.78%

20) What percent of 80 is 11.11? 13.88%

21) What percent of 82 is 10? 12.19%

22) 76 is 228% of what? 33.33

✏️ **Find the selling price of each item.**

1) Cost of a watch $21.3, markup: 63%, discount: 57%, tax: 7% :

2) Cost of a bag $24, markup: 30%, discount: 49%, tax: 6% :

3) Cost of a bag $15, markup: 44%, discount: 49%, tax: 9% :

4) Cost of a bag $33.1, markup: 65%, discount: 55%, tax: 6% :

5) Cost of a belt $8, markup: 26%, discount: 38%, tax: 5% :

6) Cost of a shirt $27.69, markup: 72%, discount: 52%, tax: 8% :

7) Cost of a wallet $25.48, markup: 77%, discount: 66%, tax: 9% :

8) Cost of a shirt $9.65, markup: 79%, discount: 69%, tax: 5% :

9) Cost of a toy $31, markup: 46%, discount: 10%, tax: 8% :

10) Cost of a toy $22, markup: 20%, discount: 35%, tax: 8% :

11) Cost of a hat $23, markup: 32%, discount: 30%, tax: 7% :

12) Cost of a bag $15.81, markup: 68%, discount: 73%, tax: 5% :

13) Cost of a shirt $9, markup: 48%, discount: 20%, tax: 8% :

✏️➤ **Find the selling price of each item.**

1) Cost of a watch $21.3, markup: 63%, discount: 57%, tax: 7% : 15.97

2) Cost of a bag $24, markup: 30%, discount: 49%, tax: 6% : 16.87

3) Cost of a bag $15, markup: 44%, discount: 49%, tax: 9% : 12.01

4) Cost of a bag $33.1, markup: 65%, discount: 55%, tax: 6% : 26.05

5) Cost of a belt $8, markup: 26%, discount: 38%, tax: 5% : 6.56

6) Cost of a shirt $27.69, markup: 72%, discount: 52%, tax: 8% : 24.68

7) Cost of a wallet $25.48, markup: 77%, discount: 66%, tax: 9% : 16.72

8) Cost of a shirt $9.65, markup: 79%, discount: 69%, tax: 5% : 5.62

9) Cost of a toy $31, markup: 46%, discount: 10%, tax: 8% : 43.99

10) Cost of a toy $22, markup: 20%, discount: 35%, tax: 8% : 18.54

11) Cost of a hat $23, markup: 32%, discount: 30%, tax: 7% : 22.74

12) Cost of a bag $15.81, markup: 68%, discount: 73%, tax: 5% : 7.53

13) Cost of a shirt $9, markup: 48%, discount: 20%, tax: 8% : 11.51

testinar.com/t/?c=4

✏️ **Use simple interest to find the ending balance.**

1) $4,400.00 at 13% for 6 years.

2) $2,150.00 at 16% for 10 years.

3) $2,550.00 at 10% for 4 years.

4) $4,850.00 at 14% for 6 years.

5) $4,200.00 at 19% for 4 years.

6) $4,550.00 at 16% for 6 years.

7) $2,600.00 at 18% for 6 years.

8) $4,650.00 at 6% for 13 years.

9) $4,600.00 at 9% for 3 years.

10) $5,500.00 at 8% for 14 years.

11) $3,400.00 at 2% for 14 years.

12) $3,150.00 at 16% for 11 years.

13) $1,950.00 at 11% for 12 years.

14) $1,450.00 at 10% for 4 years.

15) $5,350.00 at 19% for 14 years.

16) $4,450.00 at 4% for 5 years.

17) $4,700.00 at 13% for 13 years.

18) $1,200.00 at 3% for 9 years.

19) $1,350.00 at 17% for 14 years.

20) $2,800.00 at 10% for 11 years.

21) $4,100.00 at 10% for 10 years.

22) $2,950.00 at 9% for 10 years.

▱➤ **Use simple interest to find the ending balance.**

1) $4,400.00 at 13% for 6 years.
   ⇒ $7,832.00

2) $2,150.00 at 16% for 10 years.
   ⇒ $5,590.00

3) $2,550.00 at 10% for 4 years.
   ⇒ $3,570.00

4) $4,850.00 at 14% for 6 years.
   ⇒ $8,924.00

5) $4,200.00 at 19% for 4 years.
   ⇒ $7,392.00

6) $4,550.00 at 16% for 6 years.
   ⇒ $8,918.00

7) $2,600.00 at 18% for 6 years.
   ⇒ $5,408.00

8) $4,650.00 at 6% for 13 years.
   ⇒ $8,277.00

9) $4,600.00 at 9% for 3 years.
   ⇒ $5,842.00

10) $5,500.00 at 8% for 14 years.
   ⇒ $11,660.00

11) $3,400.00 at 2% for 14 years.
   ⇒ $4,352.00

12) $3,150.00 at 16% for 11 years.
   ⇒ $8,694.00

13) $1,950.00 at 11% for 12 years.
   ⇒ $4,524.00

14) $1,450.00 at 10% for 4 years.
   ⇒ $2,030.00

15) $5,350.00 at 19% for 14 years.
   ⇒ $19,581.00

16) $4,450.00 at 4% for 5 years.
   ⇒ $5,340.00

17) $4,700.00 at 13% for 13 years.
   ⇒ $12,643.00

18) $1,200.00 at 3% for 9 years.
   ⇒ $1,524.00

19) $1,350.00 at 17% for 14 years.
   ⇒ $4,563.00

20) $2,800.00 at 10% for 11 years.
   ⇒ $5,880.00

21) $4,100.00 at 10% for 10 years.
   ⇒ $8,200.00

22) $2,950.00 at 9% for 10 years.
   ⇒ $5,605.00

✏️ **Simplify each expression.**

1) $x + 4x - x$, use $x = 6$

2) $x + x(5x - x)$, use $x = 5$

3) $x + 20x - x$, use $x = 7$

4) $x + 21x$, use $x = 1$

5) $10 + x(9x - x)$, use $x = 4$

6) $x + 10x$, use $x = 5$

7) $x + 2x - x$, use $x = 1$

8) $10 + x(13x - x)$, use $x = 1$

9) $x + 3x$, use $x = 2$

10) $x + 14x - x$, use $x = 8$

11) $x + 13x$, use $x = 5$

12) $10 + x(2x - x)$, use $x = 3$

13) $x + 9x$, use $x = 8$

14) $x + 11x - x$, use $x = 6$

15) $x + 2x$, use $x = 3$

16) $x + 18x - x$, use $x = 1$

17) $x + 19x - x$, use $x = 5$

18) $x + x(20x - x)$, use $x = 4$

19) $x + x(8x - x)$, use $x = 5$

20) $x + 3x - x$, use $x = 7$

21) $x + x(12x - x)$, use $x = 7$

22) $10 + x(7x - x)$, use $x = 3$

▱ **Simplify each expression.**

1) $x + 4x - x = 24$, use $x = 6$

2) $x + x(5x - x) = 105$, use $x = 5$

3) $x + 20x - x = 140$, use $x = 7$

4) $x + 21x = 22$, use $x = 1$

5) $10 + x(9x - x) = 138$, use $x = 4$

6) $x + 10x = 55$, use $x = 5$

7) $x + 2x - x = 2$, use $x = 1$

8) $10 + x(13x - x) = 22$, use $x = 1$

9) $x + 3x = 8$, use $x = 2$

10) $x + 14x - x = 112$, use $x = 8$

11) $x + 13x = 70$, use $x = 5$

12) $10 + x(2x - x) = 19$, use $x = 3$

13) $x + 9x = 80$, use $x = 8$

14) $x + 11x - x = 66$, use $x = 6$

15) $x + 2x = 9$, use $x = 3$

16) $x + 18x - x = 18$, use $x = 1$

17) $x + 19x - x = 95$, use $x = 5$

18) $x + x(20x - x) = 308$, use $x = 4$

19) $x + x(8x - x) = 180$, use $x = 5$

20) $x + 3x - x = 21$, use $x = 7$

21) $x + x(12x - x) = 546$, use $x = 7$

22) $10 + x(7x - x) = 64$, use $x = 3$

Simplify each expression.

testinar.com/t/?c=6

1) $5x^2(5x + x) - x^3 =$

2) $21x + 7x^2 =$

3) $16x + 2x^2 =$

4) $3x^2(5x + x) + x^3 =$

5) $11x^2(5x + x) + x^3 =$

6) $4x^2(2x + x) - x^3 =$

7) $8x^2(2x) =$

8) $5x + 4x^2 =$

9) $16x^2(6x + x) =$

10) $6x + 4x^2 =$

11) $8x^2(6x + x) - x^3 =$

12) $12x + 6x^2 =$

13) $17x^2(3x + x) =$

14) $12x^2(2x + x) =$

15) $14x^2(6x + x) - x^3 =$

16) $10x + 7x^2 =$

17) $18x^2(5x) =$

18) $2x^2(4x) =$

19) $12x^2(5x + x) + x^3 =$

20) $15x^2(4x + x) =$

21) $15x^2(2x + x) - x^3 =$

22) $14x^2(4x + x) =$

▱➤ **Simplify each expression.**

1) $5x^2(5x + x) - x^3 = 29x^3$

2) $21x + 7x^2 = x(21 + 7x)$

3) $16x + 2x^2 = x(16 + 2x)$

4) $3x^2(5x + x) + x^3 = 19x^3$

5) $11x^2(5x + x) + x^3 = 67x^3$

6) $4x^2(2x + x) - x^3 = 11x^3$

7) $8x^2(2x) = 16x^3$

8) $5x + 4x^2 = x(5 + 4x)$

9) $16x^2(6x + x) = 112x^3$

10) $6x + 4x^2 = x(6 + 4x)$

11) $8x^2(6x + x) - x^3 = 55x^3$

12) $12x + 6x^2 = x(12 + 6x)$

13) $17x^2(3x + x) = 68x^3$

14) $12x^2(2x + x) = 36x^3$

15) $14x^2(6x + x) - x^3 = 97x^3$

16) $10x + 7x^2 = x(10 + 7x)$

17) $18x^2(5x) = 90x^3$

18) $2x^2(4x) = 8x^3$

19) $12x^2(5x + x) + x^3 = 73x^3$

20) $15x^2(4x + x) = 75x^3$

21) $15x^2(2x + x) - x^3 = 44x^3$

22) $14x^2(4x + x) = 70x^3$

✏️ **Simplify each polynomial.**

1) $6x + 4x^2 + x^3 + 7x - 7 =$

2) $13x^3 + 7x^2 - 4x^3 + 17x^2 - 20x^3 + 11x^2 =$

3) $11x + 3x^2 - x^3 + 5x =$

4) $19x + 6x^2 - x^3 + 3x =$

5) $(20x^3 + 7x^2 - 5x^3) + (25x^2 - 27x^3 + 12x^2) =$

6) $(8x^3 + 6x^2 - 4x^3) + (12x^2 - 14x^3 + 10x^2) =$

7) $5x^3 + 6x^2 - 3x^3 + 8x^2 - 11x^3 + 9x^2 =$

8) $(10x^3 + 5x^2 - 5x^3) + (15x^2 - 15x^3 + 10x^2) =$

9) $(11x^3 + 6x^2 - 4x^3) + (15x^2 - 17x^3 + 10x^2) =$

10) $(9x^3 + 2x^2 - 7x^3) + (16x^2 - 11x^3 + 9x^2) =$

11) $8x + 2x^2 - x^3 + 5x =$

▷ **Simplify each polynomial.**

1) $6x + 4x^2 + x^3 + 7x - 7 = x^3 + 4x^2 + 13x - 7$

2) $13x^3 + 7x^2 - 4x^3 + 17x^2 - 20x^3 + 11x^2 = -11x^3 + 35x^2$

3) $11x + 3x^2 - x^3 + 5x = -x^3 + 3x^2 + 16x$

4) $19x + 6x^2 - x^3 + 3x = -x^3 + 6x^2 + 22x$

5) $(20x^3 + 7x^2 - 5x^3) + (25x^2 - 27x^3 + 12x^2) = -12x^3 + 44x^2$

6) $(8x^3 + 6x^2 - 4x^3) + (12x^2 - 14x^3 + 10x^2) = -10x^3 + 28x^2$

7) $5x^3 + 6x^2 - 3x^3 + 8x^2 - 11x^3 + 9x^2 = -9x^3 + 23x^2$

8) $(10x^3 + 5x^2 - 5x^3) + (15x^2 - 15x^3 + 10x^2) = -10x^3 + 30x^2$

9) $(11x^3 + 6x^2 - 4x^3) + (15x^2 - 17x^3 + 10x^2) = -10x^3 + 31x^2$

10) $(9x^3 + 2x^2 - 7x^3) + (16x^2 - 11x^3 + 9x^2) = -9x^3 + 27x^2$

11) $8x + 2x^2 - x^3 + 5x = -x^3 + 2x^2 + 13x$

Use the distributive property to simplify each expression.

1) $13(15 + 4x) =$

2) $-13(13 + 3x) =$

3) $-5(6 + 8x) =$

4) $-15(17 - 3x) =$

5) $-(-19 - 2x) =$

6) $-(7 - 4x) =$

7) $-3(9 - 7x) =$

8) $20(20 + 2x) =$

9) $-15(20 + 8x) =$

10) $-6(3 - 8x) =$

11) $-17(19 - 3x) =$

12) $-(-3 - 6x) =$

13) $-5(5 + 7x) =$

14) $12(18 + 8x) =$

15) $-(-5 - 3x) =$

16) $-(-18 - 7x) =$

17) $-10(10 + 3x) =$

18) $-(13 - 3x) =$

19) $2(7 + 7x) =$

20) $-5(12 - 8x) =$

21) $-(-12 - 6x) =$

22) $-(-20 - 3x) =$

▱ **Use the distributive property to simplify each expression.**

1) $13(15 + 4x) = 52x + 195$

2) $-13(13 + 3x) = -39x - 169$

3) $-5(6 + 8x) = -40x - 30$

4) $-15(17 - 3x) = 45x - 255$

5) $-(-19 - 2x) = 2x + 19$

6) $-(7 - 4x) = 4x - 7$

7) $-3(9 - 7x) = 21x - 27$

8) $20(20 + 2x) = 40x + 400$

9) $-15(20 + 8x) = -120x - 300$

10) $-6(3 - 8x) = 48x - 18$

11) $-17(19 - 3x) = 51x - 323$

12) $-(-3 - 6x) = 6x + 3$

13) $-5(5 + 7x) = -35x - 25$

14) $12(18 + 8x) = 96x + 216$

15) $-(-5 - 3x) = 3x + 5$

16) $-(-18 - 7x) = 7x + 18$

17) $-10(10 + 3x) = -30x - 100$

18) $-(13 - 3x) = 3x - 13$

19) $2(7 + 7x) = 14x + 14$

20) $-5(12 - 8x) = 40x - 60$

21) $-(-12 - 6x) = 6x + 12$

22) $-(-20 - 3x) = 3x + 20$

testinar.com/t/?c=6

✏️ **Simplify each algebraic expression.**

1) $x = 4,\ 7x + 3 =$

2) $x = 7,\ 2(\frac{21}{x} + 3) =$

3) $x = -20,\ \frac{40}{x} + 3 =$

4) $x = 14,\ 3(\frac{56}{x} + 7) =$

5) $x = -4,\ \frac{8}{x} + 2 =$

6) $x = 9,\ 2x + 7 =$

7) $x = 13,\ 4(\frac{26}{x} - 2) =$

8) $x = 12,\ \frac{48}{x} + 6 =$

9) $x = 2,\ 2(\frac{8}{x} + 3) =$

10) $x = -13,\ \frac{52}{x} + 5 =$

11) $x = 7,\ 7x - 4 =$

12) $x = -21,\ 4x + 4 =$

13) $x = 20,\ 3(\frac{60}{x} - 2) =$

14) $x = 8,\ 4(\frac{24}{x} + 2) =$

15) $x = -3,\ \frac{12}{x} + 8 =$

16) $x = 6,\ 2(\frac{12}{x} - 6) =$

17) $x = 18,\ \frac{72}{x} + 4 =$

18) $x = 11,\ x - 5 =$

19) $x = 2,\ 4x + 8 =$

20) $x = -9,\ \frac{27}{x} + 6 =$

21) $x = 21,\ 3(\frac{84}{x} - 2) =$

22) $x = 16,\ 3x + 2 =$

✏️ **Simplify each algebraic expression.**

1) $x = 4$, $7x + 3 = 31$

2) $x = 7$, $2(\frac{21}{x} + 3) = 12$

3) $x = -20$, $\frac{40}{x} + 3 = 1$

4) $x = 14$, $3(\frac{56}{x} + 7) = 33$

5) $x = -4$, $\frac{8}{x} + 2 = 0$

6) $x = 9$, $2x + 7 = 25$

7) $x = 13$, $4(\frac{26}{x} - 2) = 0$

8) $x = 12$, $\frac{48}{x} + 6 = 10$

9) $x = 2$, $2(\frac{8}{x} + 3) = 14$

10) $x = -13$, $\frac{52}{x} + 5 = 1$

11) $x = 7$, $7x - 4 = 45$

12) $x = -21$, $4x + 4 = -80$

13) $x = 20$, $3(\frac{60}{x} - 2) = 3$

14) $x = 8$, $4(\frac{24}{x} + 2) = 20$

15) $x = -3$, $\frac{12}{x} + 8 = 4$

16) $x = 6$, $2(\frac{12}{x} - 6) = -8$

17) $x = 18$, $\frac{72}{x} + 4 = 8$

18) $x = 11$, $x - 5 = 6$

19) $x = 2$, $4x + 8 = 16$

20) $x = -9$, $\frac{27}{x} + 6 = 3$

21) $x = 21$, $3(\frac{84}{x} - 2) = 6$

22) $x = 16$, $3x + 2 = 50$

testinar.com/t/?c=6

✏️ **Simplify each algebraic expression.**

1) $x = 11, y = 4, \quad -4(3x - 4y - 11) =$

2) $x = 3, y = 2, \quad 3x + 6y - 3 =$

3) $x = 5, y = 7, \quad 4x + 20y - 5 =$

4) $x = 14, y = 3, \quad 4x(2y - 14) =$

5) $x = 8, y = 3, \quad 4x(3y - 8) =$

6) $x = 8, y = 4, \quad 2x(2y - 8) =$

7) $x = 19, y = 4, \quad 2x + \frac{12}{y} - 19 =$

8) $x = 10, y = 4, \quad 4x(3y - 10) =$

9) $x = 12, y = 5, \quad -5(2x - 3y - 12) =$

10) $x = 15, y = 4, \quad 4(4x - 3y + 15) =$

11) $x = 10, y = 3, \quad 2x + 20y - 10 =$

12) $x = 7, y = 5, \quad 2x(3y - 7) =$

13) $x = 14, y = 5, \quad 4x + 42y - 14 =$

▷ **Simplify each algebraic expression.**

1) $x = 11, y = 4, \ -4(3x - 4y - 11) = -24$

2) $x = 3, y = 2, \ 3x + 6y - 3 = 18$

3) $x = 5, y = 7, \ 4x + 20y - 5 = 155$

4) $x = 14, y = 3, \ 4x(2y - 14) = -448$

5) $x = 8, y = 3, \ 4x(3y - 8) = 32$

6) $x = 8, y = 4, \ 2x(2y - 8) = 0$

7) $x = 19, y = 4, \ 2x + \frac{12}{y} - 19 = 22$

8) $x = 10, y = 4, \ 4x(3y - 10) = 80$

9) $x = 12, y = 5, \ -5(2x - 3y - 12) = 15$

10) $x = 15, y = 4, \ 4(4x - 3y + 15) = 252$

11) $x = 10, y = 3, \ 2x + 20y - 10 = 70$

12) $x = 7, y = 5, \ 2x(3y - 7) = 112$

13) $x = 14, y = 5, \ 4x + 42y - 14 = 252$

✏️ **Simplify each expression.**

1) $9x - 3x =$

2) $4x + 3(2x - 3 + x) =$

3) $9x + (4x - 3 - x) =$

4) $13x + (-3)(2x - 3 + x) =$

5) $6x - 14x =$

6) $10x + 4x - 3 =$

7) $4x + (3x - 5 - x) =$

8) $3x + 2(4x - 2 + x) =$

9) $7x + (5x - 2 - x) =$

10) $16x + 2(5x - 2 + x) =$

11) $14x + 2x - 2 =$

12) $10x + (-4)(4x - 4 + x) =$

13) $8x + (3x - 3 - x) =$

Simplify each expression.

1) $9x - 3x = 6x$

2) $4x + 3(2x - 3 + x) = 13x - 9$

3) $9x + (4x - 3 - x) = 12x - 3$

4) $13x + (-3)(2x - 3 + x) = 4x + 9$

5) $6x - 14x = -8x$

6) $10x + 4x - 3 = 14x - 3$

7) $4x + (3x - 5 - x) = 6x - 5$

8) $3x + 2(4x - 2 + x) = 13x - 4$

9) $7x + (5x - 2 - x) = 11x - 2$

10) $16x + 2(5x - 2 + x) = 28x - 4$

11) $14x + 2x - 2 = 16x - 2$

12) $10x + (-4)(4x - 4 + x) = -10x + 16$

13) $8x + (3x - 3 - x) = 10x - 3$

One Step Equations

✏️ **Solve each equation.**

1) $x + 3 = -1$

2) $x + 2 = -4$

3) $x + 4 = -6$

4) $x + 5 = 11$

5) $x - 2 = 10$

6) $x - 3 = -2$

7) $x + 5 = -3$

8) $x - 5 = 8$

9) $x - 4 = 4$

10) $x - 5 = -5$

11) $x - 3 = -1$

12) $x + 4 = 0$

13) $x - 4 = 0$

14) $x + 2 = 7$

15) $x - 4 = 6$

16) $x - 4 = 1$

17) $x + 2 = -7$

18) $x + 4 = -8$

19) $x - 3 = 9$

20) $x - 2 = -3$

21) $x - 5 = 2$

22) $x + 4 = 6$

✏️ **Solve each equation.**

1) $x + 3 = -1 \Rightarrow x = -4$

2) $x + 2 = -4 \Rightarrow x = -6$

3) $x + 4 = -6 \Rightarrow x = -10$

4) $x + 5 = 11 \Rightarrow x = 6$

5) $x - 2 = 10 \Rightarrow x = 12$

6) $x - 3 = -2 \Rightarrow x = 1$

7) $x + 5 = -3 \Rightarrow x = -8$

8) $x - 5 = 8 \Rightarrow x = 13$

9) $x - 4 = 4 \Rightarrow x = 8$

10) $x - 5 = -5 \Rightarrow x = 0$

11) $x - 3 = -1 \Rightarrow x = 2$

12) $x + 4 = 0 \Rightarrow x = -4$

13) $x - 4 = 0 \Rightarrow x = 4$

14) $x + 2 = 7 \Rightarrow x = 5$

15) $x - 4 = 6 \Rightarrow x = 10$

16) $x - 4 = 1 \Rightarrow x = 5$

17) $x + 2 = -7 \Rightarrow x = -9$

18) $x + 4 = -8 \Rightarrow x = -12$

19) $x - 3 = 9 \Rightarrow x = 12$

20) $x - 2 = -3 \Rightarrow x = -1$

21) $x - 5 = 2 \Rightarrow x = 7$

22) $x + 4 = 6 \Rightarrow x = 2$

Solve each equation.

1) $3x - 12 = 24$

2) $3(x - 12) = 15$

3) $\frac{5x - 10}{3} = 100$

4) $4(x - 12) = 60$

5) $\frac{7x - 21}{5} = 70$

6) $4x - 12 = 24$

7) $3x - 12 = -12$

8) $\frac{4x - 8}{2} = 76$

9) $2(x - 8) = 12$

10) $\frac{2x - 8}{4} = 34$

11) $4(x - 12) = 40$

12) $\frac{5x - 20}{6} = 80$

13) $3x - 15 = -6$

14) $3x - 15 = 3$

15) $\frac{5x - 20}{6} = 60$

16) $3x - 6 = 12$

17) $\frac{5x - 25}{2} = 40$

18) $3x - 9 = -15$

19) $\frac{3x - 12}{4} = 42$

20) $\frac{2x - 6}{5} = 14$

21) $\frac{3x - 6}{3} = 12$

22) $3x - 6 = 27$

➡️ **Solve each equation.**

1) $3x - 12 = 24 \Rightarrow x = 12$

2) $3(x - 12) = 15 \Rightarrow x = 17$

3) $\frac{5x - 10}{3} = 100 \Rightarrow x = 62$

4) $4(x - 12) = 60 \Rightarrow x = 27$

5) $\frac{7x - 21}{5} = 70 \Rightarrow x = 53$

6) $4x - 12 = 24 \Rightarrow x = 9$

7) $3x - 12 = -12 \Rightarrow x = 0$

8) $\frac{4x - 8}{2} = 76 \Rightarrow x = 40$

9) $2(x - 8) = 12 \Rightarrow x = 14$

10) $\frac{2x - 8}{4} = 34 \Rightarrow x = 72$

11) $4(x - 12) = 40 \Rightarrow x = 22$

12) $\frac{5x - 20}{6} = 80 \Rightarrow x = 100$

13) $3x - 15 = -6 \Rightarrow x = 3$

14) $3x - 15 = 3 \Rightarrow x = 6$

15) $\frac{5x - 20}{6} = 60 \Rightarrow x = 76$

16) $3x - 6 = 12 \Rightarrow x = 6$

17) $\frac{5x - 25}{2} = 40 \Rightarrow x = 21$

18) $3x - 9 = -15 \Rightarrow x = -2$

19) $\frac{3x - 12}{4} = 42 \Rightarrow x = 60$

20) $\frac{2x - 6}{5} = 14 \Rightarrow x = 38$

21) $\frac{3x - 6}{3} = 12 \Rightarrow x = 14$

22) $3x - 6 = 27 \Rightarrow x = 11$

testinar.com/t/?c=7

✏️ Solve each equation.

1) $\frac{2x - 15}{7} = 48 - \frac{1}{7}x$

2) $5x - 28 = 140 - 2x$

3) $2x - 8 + 3x = 52 + x$

4) $\frac{6x - 14}{4} = 133 - \frac{1}{4}x$

5) $5x - 28 = 119 - 2x$

6) $7x - 27 = 99 - 2x$

7) $3x - 20 + 3x = 100 + x$

8) $7x - 18 + 3x = 90 + x$

9) $6x - 16 + 3x = 40 + x$

10) $3x - 20 + 3x = 35 + x$

11) $4x - 18 = 60 - 2x$

12) $7x - 18 = 117 - 2x$

13) $\frac{5x - 24}{5} = 6 - \frac{1}{5}x$

14) $4x - 30 = 12 - 2x$

15) $5x - 14 = 21 - 2x$

16) $\frac{5x - 12}{7} = 24 - \frac{1}{7}x$

17) $\frac{6x - 21}{5} = 70 - \frac{1}{5}x$

18) $\frac{1x - 10}{3} = 6 - \frac{1}{3}x$

19) $6x - 40 = 128 - 2x$

20) $\frac{3x - 16}{7} = 32 - \frac{1}{7}x$

21) $5x - 21 = 56 - 2x$

22) $5x - 21 = 49 - 2x$

✏️ **Solve each equation.**

1) $\frac{2x - 15}{7} = 48 - \frac{1}{7}x \Rightarrow x = 117$

2) $5x - 28 = 140 - 2x \Rightarrow x = 24$

3) $2x - 8 + 3x = 52 + x$
$\Rightarrow x = 15$

4) $\frac{6x - 14}{4} = 133 - \frac{1}{4}x \Rightarrow x = 78$

5) $5x - 28 = 119 - 2x \Rightarrow x = 21$

6) $7x - 27 = 99 - 2x \Rightarrow x = 14$

7) $3x - 20 + 3x = 100 + x$
$\Rightarrow x = 24$

8) $7x - 18 + 3x = 90 + x$
$\Rightarrow x = 12$

9) $6x - 16 + 3x = 40 + x$
$\Rightarrow x = 7$

10) $3x - 20 + 3x = 35 + x$
$\Rightarrow x = 11$

11) $4x - 18 = 60 - 2x \Rightarrow x = 13$

12) $7x - 18 = 117 - 2x \Rightarrow x = 15$

13) $\frac{5x - 24}{5} = 6 - \frac{1}{5}x \Rightarrow x = 9$

14) $4x - 30 = 12 - 2x \Rightarrow x = 7$

15) $5x - 14 = 21 - 2x \Rightarrow x = 5$

16) $\frac{5x - 12}{7} = 24 - \frac{1}{7}x \Rightarrow x = 30$

17) $\frac{6x - 21}{5} = 70 - \frac{1}{5}x \Rightarrow x = 53$

18) $\frac{1x - 10}{3} = 6 - \frac{1}{3}x \Rightarrow x = 14$

19) $6x - 40 = 128 - 2x \Rightarrow x = 21$

20) $\frac{3x - 16}{7} = 32 - \frac{1}{7}x \Rightarrow x = 60$

21) $5x - 21 = 56 - 2x \Rightarrow x = 11$

22) $5x - 21 = 49 - 2x \Rightarrow x = 10$

74

Solve each system of equations.

1)
$$3x + 7y = 34$$
$$3x + 2y = 14$$
$$x = \underline{\quad} \quad y = \underline{\quad}$$

2)
$$2x + 6y = -10$$
$$4x + 2y = 10$$
$$x = \underline{\quad} \quad y = \underline{\quad}$$

3)
$$5x + 2y = -3$$
$$7x + 7y = 0$$
$$x = \underline{\quad} \quad y = \underline{\quad}$$

4)
$$4x + 7y = -8$$
$$4x + 2y = 12$$
$$x = \underline{\quad} \quad y = \underline{\quad}$$

5)
$$4x + 5y = 24$$
$$2x + 4y = 18$$
$$x = \underline{\quad} \quad y = \underline{\quad}$$

6)
$$5x + 7y = -41$$
$$5x + 5y = -35$$
$$x = \underline{\quad} \quad y = \underline{\quad}$$

7)
$$4x + 2y = -20$$
$$5x + 4y = -28$$
$$x = \underline{\quad} \quad y = \underline{\quad}$$

8)
$$2x + 2y = 4$$
$$4x + 4y = 8$$
$$x = \underline{\quad} \quad y = \underline{\quad}$$

9)
$$2x + 6y = -6$$
$$7x + 6y = 9$$
$$x = \underline{\quad} \quad y = \underline{\quad}$$

10)
$$4x + 3y = -2$$
$$7x + 3y = -8$$
$$x = \underline{\quad} \quad y = \underline{\quad}$$

11)
$$2x + 5y = 30$$
$$7x + 7y = 63$$
$$x = \underline{\quad} \quad y = \underline{\quad}$$

12)
$$4x + 4y = 0$$
$$3x + 7y = -16$$
$$x = \underline{\quad} \quad y = \underline{\quad}$$

13)
$$4x + 4y = 20$$
$$2x + 6y = 30$$
$$x = \underline{\quad} \quad y = \underline{\quad}$$

14)
$$4x + 3y = -18$$
$$3x + 2y = -13$$
$$x = \underline{\quad} \quad y = \underline{\quad}$$

15)
$$4x + 3y = 1$$
$$4x + 2y = 2$$
$$x = \underline{\quad} \quad y = \underline{\quad}$$

16)
$$5x + 3y = 10$$
$$5x + 5y = 20$$
$$x = \underline{\quad} \quad y = \underline{\quad}$$

Solve each system of equations.

1) $$3x + 7y = 34$$
$$3x + 2y = 14$$
$$\overline{\quad x = 2 \quad y = 4 \quad}$$

2) $$2x + 6y = -10$$
$$4x + 2y = 10$$
$$\overline{\quad x = 4 \quad y = -3 \quad}$$

3) $$5x + 2y = -3$$
$$7x + 7y = 0$$
$$\overline{\quad x = -1 \quad y = 1 \quad}$$

4) $$4x + 7y = -8$$
$$4x + 2y = 12$$
$$\overline{\quad x = 5 \quad y = -4 \quad}$$

5) $$4x + 5y = 24$$
$$2x + 4y = 18$$
$$\overline{\quad x = 1 \quad y = 4 \quad}$$

6) $$5x + 7y = -41$$
$$5x + 5y = -35$$
$$\overline{\quad x = -4 \quad y = -3 \quad}$$

7) $$4x + 2y = -20$$
$$5x + 4y = -28$$
$$\overline{\quad x = -4 \quad y = -2 \quad}$$

8) $$2x + 2y = 4$$
$$4x + 4y = 8$$
$$\overline{\quad x = -2 \quad y = 4 \quad}$$

9) $$2x + 6y = -6$$
$$7x + 6y = 9$$
$$\overline{\quad x = 3 \quad y = -2 \quad}$$

10) $$4x + 3y = -2$$
$$7x + 3y = -8$$
$$\overline{\quad x = -2 \quad y = 2 \quad}$$

11) $$2x + 5y = 30$$
$$7x + 7y = 63$$
$$\overline{\quad x = 5 \quad y = 4 \quad}$$

12) $$4x + 4y = 0$$
$$3x + 7y = -16$$
$$\overline{\quad x = 4 \quad y = -4 \quad}$$

13) $$4x + 4y = 20$$
$$2x + 6y = 30$$
$$\overline{\quad x = 0 \quad y = 5 \quad}$$

14) $$4x + 3y = -18$$
$$3x + 2y = -13$$
$$\overline{\quad x = -3 \quad y = -2 \quad}$$

15) $$4x + 3y = 1$$
$$4x + 2y = 2$$
$$\overline{\quad x = 1 \quad y = -1 \quad}$$

16) $$5x + 3y = 10$$
$$5x + 5y = 20$$
$$\overline{\quad x = -1 \quad y = 5 \quad}$$

✏️▷ **Solve each word problem.**

1) At a store, Eva bought 5 shirts and 5 hats for $45. Nicole bought 7 same shirts and 6 same hats for $59. What is the price of each shirt?

2) A theater is selling tickets for a performance. Mr. Smith purchased 5 senior tickets and 7 child tickets for $58 for his friends and family. Mr. Jackson purchased 7 senior tickets and 6 child tickets for $66. What is the price of a senior ticket?

3) Emma and Sepehr are selling Chocolate Chip cookies and Oreo cookies Emma sold 6 boxes of Chocolate Chip cookies and 3 boxes of Oreo cookies for a total of $48. Sepehr sold 2 boxes of Chocolate Chip cookies and 2 boxes of Oreo cookies for a total of $22. Find the cost of one box of Chocolate Chip cookies.

4) Emma and Sepehr are selling Chocolate Chip cookies and Oreo cookies Emma sold 2 boxes of Chocolate Chip cookies and 6 boxes of Oreo cookies for a total of $44. Sepehr sold 3 boxes of Chocolate Chip cookies and 2 boxes of Oreo cookies for a total of $24. Find the cost of one box of Chocolate Chip cookies.

5) Tickets to a movie cost $5 for adults and $4 for students. A group of friends purchased 12 tickets for $54. How many adults ticket did they buy?

6) Tickets to a movie cost $2 for adults and $2 for students. A group of friends purchased 10 tickets for $20. How many adults ticket did they buy?

7) At a store, Eva bought 3 shirts and 2 hats for $20. Nicole bought 7 same shirts and 2 same hats for $36. What is the price of each shirt?

8) A theater is selling tickets for a performance. Mr. Smith purchased 5 senior tickets and 6 child tickets for $50 for his friends and family. Mr. Jackson purchased 3 senior tickets and 5 child tickets for $37. What is the price of a senior ticket?

✏️ **Solve each word problem.**

1) At a store, Eva bought 5 shirts and 5 hats for $45. Nicole bought 7 same shirts and 6 same hats for $59. What is the price of each shirt? $5

2) A theater is selling tickets for a performance. Mr. Smith purchased 5 senior tickets and 7 child tickets for $58 for his friends and family. Mr. Jackson purchased 7 senior tickets and 6 child tickets for $66. What is the price of a senior ticket? $6

3) Emma and Sepehr are selling Chocolate Chip cookies and Oreo cookies Emma sold 6 boxes of Chocolate Chip cookies and 3 boxes of Oreo cookies for a total of $48. Sepehr sold 2 boxes of Chocolate Chip cookies and 2 boxes of Oreo cookies for a total of $22. Find the cost of one box of Chocolate Chip cookies. 5

4) Emma and Sepehr are selling Chocolate Chip cookies and Oreo cookies Emma sold 2 boxes of Chocolate Chip cookies and 6 boxes of Oreo cookies for a total of $44. Sepehr sold 3 boxes of Chocolate Chip cookies and 2 boxes of Oreo cookies for a total of $24. Find the cost of one box of Chocolate Chip cookies. 4

5) Tickets to a movie cost $5 for adults and $4 for students. A group of friends purchased 12 tickets for $54. How many adults ticket did they buy? 6 tickets.

6) Tickets to a movie cost $2 for adults and $2 for students. A group of friends purchased 10 tickets for $20. How many adults ticket did they buy? 6 tickets.

7) At a store, Eva bought 3 shirts and 2 hats for $20. Nicole bought 7 same shirts and 2 same hats for $36. What is the price of each shirt? $4

8) A theater is selling tickets for a performance. Mr. Smith purchased 5 senior tickets and 6 child tickets for $50 for his friends and family. Mr. Jackson purchased 3 senior tickets and 5 child tickets for $37. What is the price of a senior ticket? $4

Multiply.

1) $(x + 5)(x + 4) =$

2) $(x + 8)(x + 1) =$

3) $(x + 2)(x - 2) =$

4) $(x + 1)(x + 4) =$

5) $(x + 1)(x + 2) =$

6) $(x + 2)(x + 5) =$

7) $(x - 5)(x - 1) =$

8) $(x + 3)(x + 5) =$

9) $(x - 5)(x + 3) =$

10) $(x - 1)(x + 3) =$

11) $(x - 5)(x + 5) =$

12) $(x - 5)(x - 2) =$

13) $(x + 5)(x - 2) =$

14) $(x - 1)(x - 3) =$

15) $(x - 1)(x + 5) =$

16) $(x - 4)(x + 8) =$

17) $(x + 3)(x + 2) =$

18) $(x - 2)(x - 4) =$

19) $(x + 2)(x + 4) =$

20) $(x + 8)(x + 3) =$

21) $(x + 1)(x - 5) =$

22) $(x + 3)(x - 2) =$

> **Multiply.**

1) $(x + 5)(x + 4) = x^2 + 9x + 20$ 2) $(x + 8)(x + 1) = x^2 + 9x + 8$

3) $(x + 2)(x - 2) = x^2 + 0x - 4$ 4) $(x + 1)(x + 4) = x^2 + 5x + 4$

5) $(x + 1)(x + 2) = x^2 + 3x + 2$ 6) $(x + 2)(x + 5) = x^2 + 7x + 10$

7) $(x - 5)(x - 1) = x^2 - 6x + 5$ 8) $(x + 3)(x + 5) = x^2 + 8x + 15$

9) $(x - 5)(x + 3) = x^2 - 2x - 15$ 10) $(x - 1)(x + 3) = x^2 + 2x - 3$

11) $(x - 5)(x + 5) = x^2 + 0x - 25$ 12) $(x - 5)(x - 2) = x^2 - 7x + 10$

13) $(x + 5)(x - 2) = x^2 + 3x - 10$ 14) $(x - 1)(x - 3) = x^2 - 4x + 3$

15) $(x - 1)(x + 5) = x^2 + 4x - 5$ 16) $(x - 4)(x + 8) = x^2 + 4x - 32$

17) $(x + 3)(x + 2) = x^2 + 5x + 6$ 18) $(x - 2)(x - 4) = x^2 - 6x + 8$

19) $(x + 2)(x + 4) = x^2 + 6x + 8$ 20) $(x + 8)(x + 3) = x^2 + 11x + 24$

21) $(x + 1)(x - 5) = x^2 - 4x - 5$ 22) $(x + 3)(x - 2) = x^2 + 1x - 6$

testinar.com/t/?c=8

✏️ **Graph each inequality.**

1) $6 \leqslant x$

2) $-10 \leqslant x$

3) $-4 \leqslant x$

4) $-2 \geqslant x$

5) $-3 < x$

6) $9 \geqslant x$

7) $8 > x$

8) $7 \leqslant x$

9) $-1 > x$

10) $-9 > x$

11) $7 \geqslant x$

12) $1 > x$

13) $-6 < x$

14) $-9 < x$

81

✏️ **Graph each inequality.**

1) $6 \leqslant x$

2) $-10 \leqslant x$

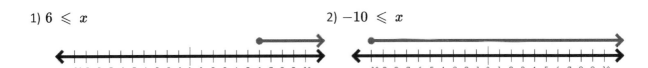

3) $-4 \leqslant x$

4) $-2 \geqslant x$

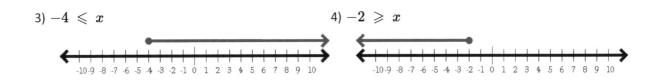

5) $-3 < x$

6) $9 \geqslant x$

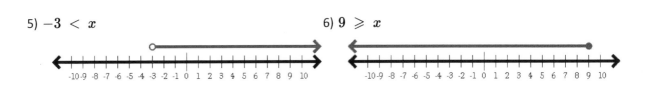

7) $8 > x$

8) $7 \leqslant x$

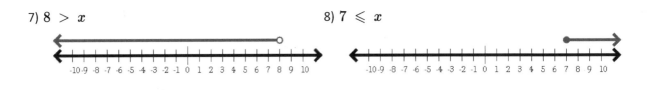

9) $-1 > x$

10) $-9 > x$

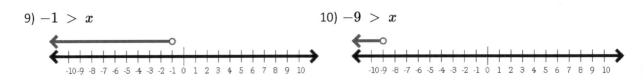

11) $7 \geqslant x$

12) $1 > x$

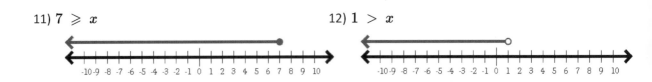

13) $-6 < x$

14) $-9 < x$

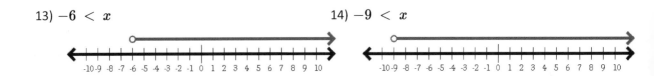

 Draw a graph for each inequality.

1) $8 < 8 + x$

2) $3 \leqslant 2 + x$

3) $7 + x \leqslant 4$

4) $6x \leqslant 30$

5) $15x > 30$

6) $4x \leqslant 32$

7) $8 + x \leqslant 2$

8) $10x \geqslant 50$

9) $14x < 56$

10) $8x \geqslant 8$

11) $3x < 18$

12) $11x \geqslant 33$

13) $14x > 56$

14) $9x \leqslant 45$

✏️ **Draw a graph for each inequality.**

1) $8 < 8 + x$

2) $3 \leqslant 2 + x$

3) $7 + x \leqslant 4$

4) $6x \leqslant 30$

5) $15x > 30$

6) $4x \leqslant 32$

7) $8 + x \leqslant 2$

8) $10x \geqslant 50$

9) $14x < 56$

10) $8x \geqslant 8$

11) $3x < 18$

12) $11x \geqslant 33$

13) $14x > 56$

14) $9x \leqslant 45$

✎ **Draw a graph for each inequality.**

1) $-5x + 6 \leqslant -34$

2) $-3x + 19 > 4$

3) $-3x + 10 > -2$

4) $-6x + 7 \geqslant -11$

5) $-4x + 7 < 3$

6) $7x + 7 \geqslant 35$

7) $3x + 13 \leqslant 25$

8) $-9x + 5 < -22$

9) $-8x + 17 \leqslant 9$

10) $-5x + 3 \geqslant -2$

11) $8x + 19 \geqslant 51$

12) $-9x + 18 \leqslant -18$

13) $6x + 9 \leqslant 45$

14) $-7x + 7 > -42$

✏️ **Draw a graph for each inequality.**

1) $-5x + 6 \leqslant -34$

2) $-3x + 19 > 4$

3) $-3x + 10 > -2$

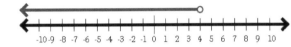

4) $-6x + 7 \geqslant -11$

5) $-4x + 7 < 3$

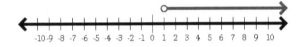

6) $7x + 7 \geqslant 35$

7) $3x + 13 \leqslant 25$

8) $-9x + 5 < -22$

9) $-8x + 17 \leqslant 9$

10) $-5x + 3 \geqslant -2$

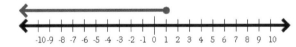

11) $8x + 19 \geqslant 51$

12) $-9x + 18 \leqslant -18$

13) $6x + 9 \leqslant 45$

14) $-7x + 7 > -42$

86

✏️ **Draw a graph for each inequality.**

1) $8(x + 11) < 136$

2) $4(x + 2) \leqslant 32$

3) $2(x + 19) < 42$

4) $3(x + 6) \leqslant 39$

5) $4(x + 9) < 40$

6) $2(x + 1) \geqslant 10$

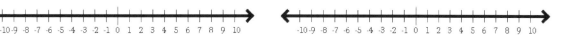

7) $\frac{x - 32}{4} \geqslant -8$

8) $\frac{x - 24}{3} \geqslant -8$

9) $6(x + 2) \geqslant 54$

10) $\frac{x - 6}{3} \geqslant -2$

11) $2(x + 3) \geqslant 20$

12) $5(x + 4) < 25$

13) $\frac{x - 18}{2} \geqslant -7$

14) $7(x + 15) \geqslant 126$

✏️ **Draw a graph for each inequality.**

1) $8(x + 11) < 136$

2) $4(x + 2) \leqslant 32$

3) $2(x + 19) < 42$

4) $3(x + 6) \leqslant 39$

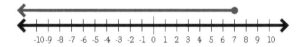

5) $4(x + 9) < 40$

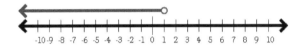

6) $2(x + 1) \geqslant 10$

7) $\frac{x - 32}{4} \geqslant -8$

8) $\frac{x - 24}{3} \geqslant -8$

9) $6(x + 2) \geqslant 54$

10) $\frac{x - 6}{3} \geqslant -2$

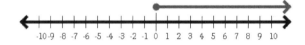

11) $2(x + 3) \geqslant 20$

12) $5(x + 4) < 25$

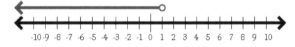

13) $\frac{x - 18}{2} \geqslant -7$

14) $7(x + 15) \geqslant 126$

testinar.com/t/?c=12

✎ **Simplify.**

1) $5x^2 \times 4yx^4 =$

2) $8x^7 \times x^5 \times x =$

3) $3x^2 \times 4yx^3 =$

4) $5y^4x^2 \times 3y^3x^4 =$

5) $4^3 \times 4 =$

6) $3y^7x^4 \times 4y^3x^4 =$

7) $5x^4 \times x^6 \times x =$

8) $(2x^3)^2 =$

9) $8y^7x^2 \times 3y^4x^3 =$

10) $6^6 \times 6 =$

11) $(10x^3)^2 =$

12) $8^4 \times 8^6 =$

13) $10^5 \times 10 =$

14) $3x^2 \times x^3 \times x =$

15) $9y^2x^4 \times 4y^2x^4 =$

16) $(8x^6)^2 =$

17) $2x^2 \times 3yx^6 =$

18) $11^7 \times 11^4 =$

19) $3^7 \times 3 =$

20) $8^3 \times 8 =$

21) $9x^4 \times 3yx^5 =$

22) $8x^5 \times 2yx^4 =$

▱⟩ **Simplify.**

1) $5x^2 \times 4yx^4 = 20yx^6$

2) $8x^7 \times x^5 \times x = 8x^{13}$

3) $3x^2 \times 4yx^3 = 12yx^5$

4) $5y^4x^2 \times 3y^3x^4 = 15y^7x^6$

5) $4^3 \times 4 = 4^4$

6) $3y^7x^4 \times 4y^3x^4 = 12y^{10}x^8$

7) $5x^4 \times x^6 \times x = 5x^{11}$

8) $(2x^3)^2 = 4x^6$

9) $8y^7x^2 \times 3y^4x^3 = 24y^{11}x^5$

10) $6^6 \times 6 = 6^7$

11) $(10x^3)^2 = 100x^6$

12) $8^4 \times 8^6 = 8^{10}$

13) $10^5 \times 10 = 10^6$

14) $3x^2 \times x^3 \times x = 3x^6$

15) $9y^2x^4 \times 4y^2x^4 = 36y^4x^8$

16) $(8x^6)^2 = 64x^{12}$

17) $2x^2 \times 3yx^6 = 6yx^8$

18) $11^7 \times 11^4 = 11^{11}$

19) $3^7 \times 3 = 3^8$

20) $8^3 \times 8 = 8^4$

21) $9x^4 \times 3yx^5 = 27yx^9$

22) $8x^5 \times 2yx^4 = 16yx^9$

Simplify.

1) $\dfrac{20x^{-6}}{2x^{-3}y^2} =$

2) $\dfrac{12x^{-6}}{4x^{-4}y^4} =$

3) $\dfrac{6x^6}{2x^3} =$

4) $\dfrac{24x^{-7}}{3x^{-3}} =$

5) $\dfrac{33x^{-8}}{3x^{-4}} =$

6) $\dfrac{18x^{-6}}{2x^{-2}} =$

7) $\dfrac{7^6}{7} =$

8) $\dfrac{18x^{-7}}{3x^{-4}y^3} =$

9) $\dfrac{8x^{-7}}{2x^{-3}} =$

10) $\dfrac{10x^{\,8}}{2x^{-3}y^2} =$

11) $\dfrac{14x^{-8}}{2x^{-4}} =$

12) $\dfrac{16x^6}{4x^3} =$

13) $\dfrac{21x^7}{3x^3} =$

14) $\dfrac{12x^{-7}}{3x^{-4}y^3} =$

15) $\dfrac{20x^{-8}}{4x^{-3}} =$

16) $\dfrac{2^6}{2} =$

17) $\dfrac{6^7}{6} =$

18) $\dfrac{11^6}{11} =$

19) $\dfrac{10^3}{10} =$

20) $\dfrac{20x^8}{2x^4} =$

21) $\dfrac{18x^7}{3x^2} =$

22) $\dfrac{16x^7}{2x^2} =$

✏️ **Simplify.**

1) $\dfrac{20x^{-6}}{2x^{-3}y^2} = \dfrac{10}{x^3 y^2}$

2) $\dfrac{12x^{-6}}{4x^{-4}y^4} = \dfrac{3}{x^2 y^4}$

3) $\dfrac{6x^6}{2x^3} = 3x^3$

4) $\dfrac{24x^{-7}}{3x^{-3}} = \dfrac{8}{x^4}$

5) $\dfrac{33x^{-8}}{3x^{-4}} = \dfrac{11}{x^4}$

6) $\dfrac{18x^{-6}}{2x^{-2}} = \dfrac{9}{x^4}$

7) $\dfrac{7^6}{7} = 7^5$

8) $\dfrac{18x^{-7}}{3x^{-4}y^3} = \dfrac{6}{x^3 y^3}$

9) $\dfrac{8x^{-7}}{2x^{-3}} = \dfrac{4}{x^4}$

10) $\dfrac{10x^{-8}}{2x^{-3}y^2} = \dfrac{5}{x^5 y^2}$

11) $\dfrac{14x^{-8}}{2x^{-4}} = \dfrac{7}{x^4}$

12) $\dfrac{16x^6}{4x^3} = 4x^3$

13) $\dfrac{21x^7}{3x^3} = 7x^4$

14) $\dfrac{12x^{-7}}{3x^{-4}y^3} = \dfrac{4}{x^3 y^3}$

15) $\dfrac{20x^{-8}}{4x^{-3}} = \dfrac{5}{x^5}$

16) $\dfrac{2^6}{2} = 2^5$

17) $\dfrac{6^7}{6} = 6^6$

18) $\dfrac{11^6}{11} = 11^5$

19) $\dfrac{10^3}{10} = 10^2$

20) $\dfrac{20x^8}{2x^4} = 10x^4$

21) $\dfrac{18x^7}{3x^2} = 6x^5$

22) $\dfrac{16x^7}{2x^2} = 8x^5$

testinar.com/t/?c=12

✎ **Simplify.**

1) $(-2x^4)^2 =$

2) $(-x^4x^2)^2 =$

3) $(9x^2y)^3 =$

4) $(-3x^3y)^2 =$

5) $(x^3y)^2 =$

6) $(-x^3)^2 =$

7) $(-6x^3y)^2 =$

8) $(5x^2y)^3 =$

9) $(-2x^4y)^2 =$

10) $(-10x^4y)^3 =$

11) $(-3x^2x^2)^3 =$

12) $(7x^3)^3 =$

13) $(x^4)^2 =$

14) $(-9x^2)^3 =$

15) $(8x^3y)^2 =$

16) $(3x^4x^2)^2 =$

17) $(2x^2x^2)^3 =$

18) $(-10x^4)^2 =$

19) $(8x^4x^2)^3 =$

20) $(x^4x^2)^2 =$

21) $(3x^4y)^3 =$

22) $(-7x^2y)^2 =$

✏️ **Simplify.**

1) $(-2x^4)^2 = 4x^8$

2) $(-x^4x^2)^2 = 1x^{12}$

3) $(9x^2y)^3 = 729x^6y^3$

4) $(-3x^3y)^2 = 9x^6y^2$

5) $(x^3y)^2 = 1x^6y^2$

6) $(-x^3)^2 = 1x^6$

7) $(-6x^3y)^2 = 36x^6y^2$

8) $(5x^2y)^3 = 125x^6y^3$

9) $(-2x^4y)^2 = 4x^8y^2$

10) $(-10x^4y)^3 = -1000x^{12}y^3$

11) $(-3x^2x^2)^3 = -27x^{12}$

12) $(7x^3)^3 = 343x^9$

13) $(x^4)^2 = 1x^8$

14) $(-9x^2)^3 = -729x^6$

15) $(8x^3y)^2 = 64x^6y^2$

16) $(3x^4x^2)^2 = 9x^{12}$

17) $(2x^2x^2)^3 = 8x^{12}$

18) $(-10x^4)^2 = 100x^8$

19) $(8x^4x^2)^3 = 512x^{18}$

20) $(x^4x^2)^2 = 1x^{12}$

21) $(3x^4y)^3 = 27x^{12}y^3$

22) $(-7x^2y)^2 = 49x^4y^2$

✏️ **Evaluate the following expressions.**

1) $9^{-4} =$

2) $2^{-2} =$

3) $0^4 =$

4) $10^{-2} =$

5) $4^{-5} =$

6) $0^6 =$

7) $0^5 =$

8) $10^{-5} =$

9) $-5^{-3} =$

10) $0^3 =$

11) $-7^{-2} =$

12) $8^{-2} =$

13) $5^{-3} =$

14) $12^{-4} =$

15) $-3^{-5} =$

16) $7^{-3} =$

17) $0^2 =$

18) $-12^{-4} =$

19) $0^7 =$

20) $10^{-4} =$

21) $10^{-3} =$

22) $-9^{-3} =$

✏️➤ **Evaluate the following expressions.**

1) $9^{-4} = \frac{1}{9^4}$

2) $2^{-2} = \frac{1}{2^2}$

3) $0^4 = 0$

4) $10^{-2} = \frac{1}{100}$

5) $4^{-5} = \frac{1}{4^5}$

6) $0^6 = 0$

7) $0^5 = 0$

8) $10^{-5} = \frac{1}{100000}$

9) $-5^{-3} = \frac{1}{-5^3}$

10) $0^3 = 0$

11) $-7^{-2} = \frac{1}{-7^2}$

12) $8^{-2} = \frac{1}{8^2}$

13) $5^{-3} = \frac{1}{5^3}$

14) $12^{-4} = \frac{1}{12^4}$

15) $-3^{-5} = \frac{1}{-3^5}$

16) $7^{-3} = \frac{1}{7^3}$

17) $0^2 = 0$

18) $-12^{-4} = \frac{1}{-12^4}$

19) $0^7 = 0$

20) $10^{-4} = \frac{1}{10000}$

21) $10^{-3} = \frac{1}{1000}$

22) $-9^{-3} = \frac{1}{-9^3}$

✏️ **Simplify.**

1) $\left(\frac{-7}{2}\right)^{-2} =$

2) $\frac{6x^3}{-2y^{-4}} =$

3) $-\frac{9x}{x^{-5}} =$

4) $-\frac{4x}{x^{-4}} =$

5) $\frac{3x^3}{-4y^{-2}} =$

6) $-\frac{2x}{x^{-2}} =$

7) $\frac{19x^3}{-2y^{-5}} =$

8) $-\frac{10x}{x^{-2}} =$

9) $-\frac{8}{x^{-3}} =$

10) $-\frac{21x}{x^{-4}} =$

11) $-\frac{3x}{x^{-4}} =$

12) $-\frac{16}{x^{-4}} =$

13) $-\frac{20}{x^{-3}} =$

14) $-\frac{11x}{x^{-3}} =$

15) $\left(\frac{4}{3}\right)^{-2} =$

16) $-\frac{10}{x^{-5}} =$

17) $-\frac{17}{x^{-3}} =$

18) $\left(\frac{12}{3}\right)^{-2} =$

19) $\left(\frac{3}{4}\right)^{-2} =$

20) $\left(\frac{-3}{3}\right)^{-2} =$

21) $-\frac{11}{x^{-3}} =$

22) $-\frac{19x}{x^{-3}} =$

✏️ **Simplify.**

1) $\left(\frac{-7}{2}\right)^{-2} = \frac{4}{49}$

2) $\frac{6x^3}{-2y^{-4}} = -\frac{6x^3y^4}{2}$

3) $-\frac{9x}{x^{-5}} = -9x^6$

4) $-\frac{4x}{x^{-4}} = -4x^5$

5) $\frac{3x^3}{-4y^{-2}} = -\frac{3x^3y^2}{4}$

6) $-\frac{2x}{x^{-2}} = -2x^3$

7) $\frac{19x^3}{-2y^{-5}} = -\frac{19x^3y^5}{2}$

8) $-\frac{10x}{x^{-2}} = -10x^3$

9) $-\frac{8}{x^{-3}} = -8x^3$

10) $-\frac{21x}{x^{-4}} = -21x^5$

11) $-\frac{3x}{x^{-4}} = -3x^5$

12) $-\frac{16}{x^{-4}} = -16x^4$

13) $-\frac{20}{x^{-3}} = -20x^3$

14) $-\frac{11x}{x^{-3}} = -11x^4$

15) $\left(\frac{4}{3}\right)^{-2} = \frac{9}{16}$

16) $-\frac{10}{x^{-5}} = -10x^5$

17) $-\frac{17}{x^{-3}} = -17x^3$

18) $\left(\frac{12}{3}\right)^{-2} = \frac{9}{144}$

19) $\left(\frac{3}{4}\right)^{-2} = \frac{16}{9}$

20) $\left(\frac{-3}{3}\right)^{-2} = \frac{9}{9}$

21) $-\frac{11}{x^{-3}} = -11x^3$

22) $-\frac{19x}{x^{-3}} = -19x^4$

✏️ **Solve.**

1) $\sqrt{324} =$

2) $\sqrt{100} =$

3) $\sqrt{245} =$

4) $\sqrt{300} =$

5) $\sqrt{1} =$

6) $\sqrt{16} =$

7) $\sqrt{45} =$

8) $\sqrt{49} =$

9) $\sqrt{363} =$

10) $\sqrt{144} =$

11) $\sqrt{9} =$

12) $\sqrt{4} =$

13) $\sqrt{72} =$

14) $\sqrt{588} =$

15) $\sqrt{81} =$

16) $\sqrt{192} =$

17) $\sqrt{32} =$

18) $\sqrt{64} =$

19) $\sqrt{169} =$

20) $\sqrt{25} =$

21) $\sqrt{121} =$

22) $\sqrt{100} =$

Answers of Square Roots

✏️ **Solve.**

1) $\sqrt{324} = 9\sqrt{4}$

2) $\sqrt{100} = 10$

3) $\sqrt{245} = 7\sqrt{5}$

4) $\sqrt{300} = 10\sqrt{3}$

5) $\sqrt{1} = 1$

6) $\sqrt{16} = 4$

7) $\sqrt{45} = 3\sqrt{5}$

8) $\sqrt{49} = 7$

9) $\sqrt{363} = 11\sqrt{3}$

10) $\sqrt{144} = 12$

11) $\sqrt{9} = 3$

12) $\sqrt{4} = 2$

13) $\sqrt{72} = 6\sqrt{2}$

14) $\sqrt{588} = 14\sqrt{3}$

15) $\sqrt{81} = 9$

16) $\sqrt{192} = 8\sqrt{3}$

17) $\sqrt{32} = 4\sqrt{2}$

18) $\sqrt{64} = 8$

19) $\sqrt{169} = 13$

20) $\sqrt{25} = 5$

21) $\sqrt{121} = 11$

22) $\sqrt{100} = 5\sqrt{4}$

testinar.com/t/?c=9

✏️ **Sketch the graph of each line.**

1) $y = -2x + 4$

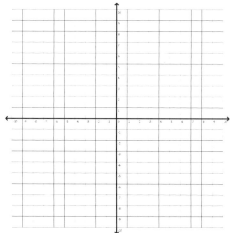

2) $y = x + 2$

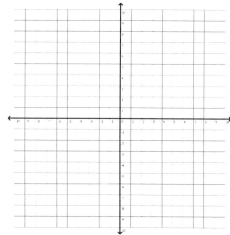

3) $y = -4x - 1$

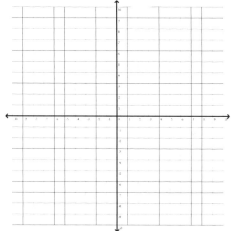

4) $y = 2x - 3$

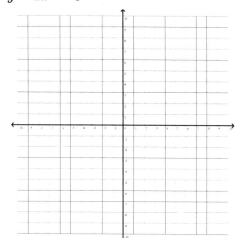

5) $y = 6x - 3$

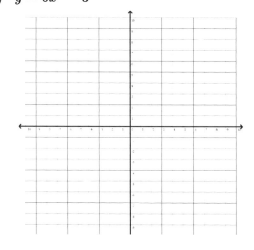

6) $y = -2x - 5$

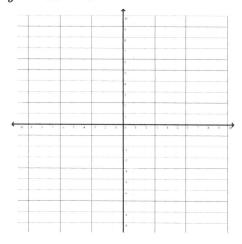

✏️ **Sketch the graph of each line.**

1) $y = -2x + 4$

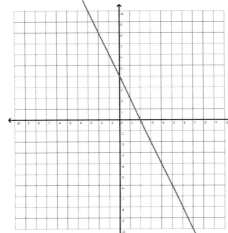

2) $y = x + 2$

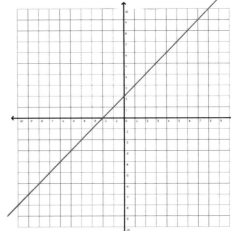

3) $y = -4x - 1$

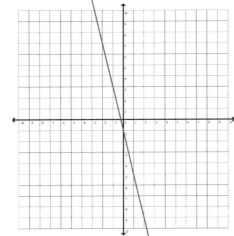

4) $y = 2x - 3$

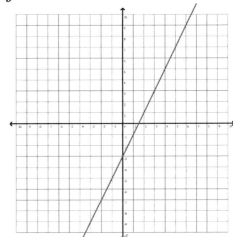

5) $y = 6x - 3$

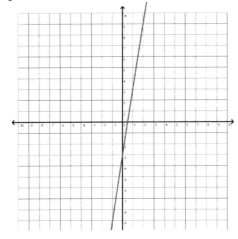

6) $y = -2x - 5$

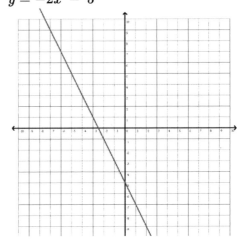

testinar.com/t/?c=9

✎▷ **Sketch the graph of each line.**

1) $-24x + 4y - 16 = 0$

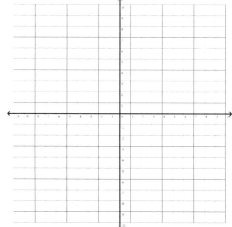

2) $-8x - 4y - 16 = 0$

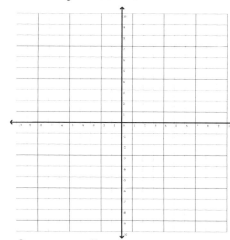

3) $4x - y - 2 = 0$

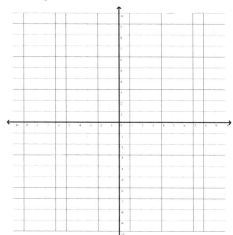

4) $-2x - y - 5 = 0$

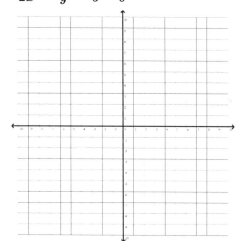

5) $6x - y - 4 = 0$

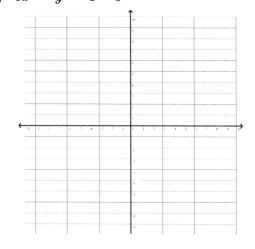

6) $3x - y - 2 = 0$

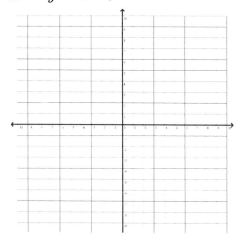

✏️➤ **Sketch the graph of each line.**

1) $-24x + 4y - 16 = 0$

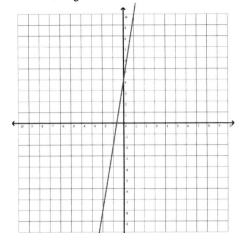

2) $-8x - 4y - 16 = 0$

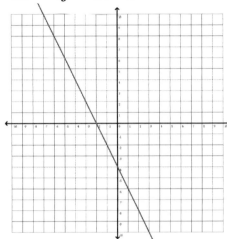

3) $4x - y - 2 = 0$

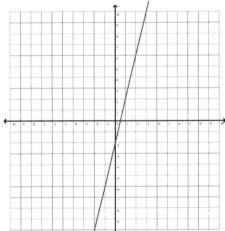

4) $-2x - y - 5 = 0$

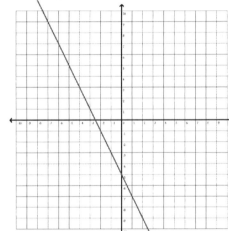

5) $6x - y - 4 = 0$

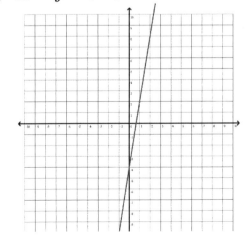

6) $3x - y - 2 = 0$

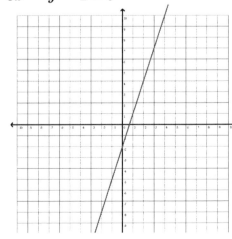

testinar.com/t/?c=9

✏️ **Find the equation of the line passing through the given points.**

1) $(8, 1)(9, 1)$

2) $(5, 6)(6, 3)$

3) $(7, 1)(8, 5)$

4) $(6, 7)(7, -6)$

5) $(6, 4)(7, 0)$

6) $(9, 1)(10, 4)$

7) $(4, 8)(5, 0)$

8) $(2, 7)(3, -1)$

9) $(5, 3)(6, -2)$

10) $(8, 10)(9, -4)$

11) $(7, 8)(8, -1)$

12) $(7, 6)(8, -5)$

13) $(5, 2)(6, -1)$

14) $(10, 7)(11, -1)$

15) $(8, 9)(9, 1)$

16) $(1, 10)(2, -6)$

17) $(3, 4)(4, 1)$

18) $(7, 4)(8, -6)$

19) $(2, 4)(3, -3)$

20) $(10, 2)(11, 3)$

21) $(6, 6)(7, -4)$

22) $(3, 8)(4, 3)$

▱▷ **Find the equation of the line passing through the given points.**

1) $(8, 1)(9, 1) \Rightarrow y = 0x + 1$

2) $(5, 6)(6, 3) \Rightarrow y = -3x + 21$

3) $(7, 1)(8, 5) \Rightarrow y = 4x - 27$

4) $(6, 7)(7, -6) \Rightarrow y = -13x + 85$

5) $(6, 4)(7, 0) \Rightarrow y = -4x + 28$

6) $(9, 1)(10, 4) \Rightarrow y = 3x - 26$

7) $(4, 8)(5, 0) \Rightarrow y = -8x + 40$

8) $(2, 7)(3, -1) \Rightarrow y = -8x + 23$

9) $(5, 3)(6, -2) \Rightarrow y = -5x + 28$

10) $(8, 10)(9, -4) \Rightarrow y = -14x + 122$

11) $(7, 8)(8, -1) \Rightarrow y = -9x + 71$

12) $(7, 6)(8, -5) \Rightarrow y = -11x + 83$

13) $(5, 2)(6, -1) \Rightarrow y = -3x + 17$

14) $(10, 7)(11, -1) \Rightarrow y = -8x + 87$

15) $(8, 9)(9, 1) \Rightarrow y = -8x + 73$

16) $(1, 10)(2, -6) \Rightarrow y = -16x + 26$

17) $(3, 4)(4, 1) \Rightarrow y = -3x + 13$

18) $(7, 4)(8, -6) \Rightarrow y = -10x + 74$

19) $(2, 4)(3, -3) \Rightarrow y = -7x + 18$

20) $(10, 2)(11, 3) \Rightarrow y = x - 8$

21) $(6, 6)(7, -4) \Rightarrow y = -10x + 66$

22) $(3, 8)(4, 3) \Rightarrow y = -5x + 23$

✏️ **Sketch the graph of each linear inequality.**

1) $y < -5x + 1$

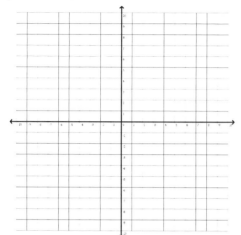

2) $y < 6x$

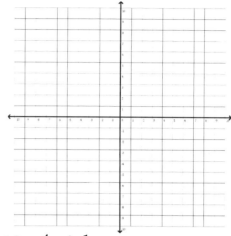

3) $y > x + 2$

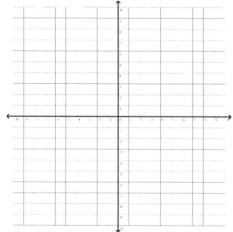

4) $y > -4x + 1$

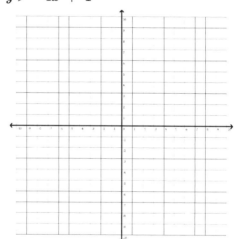

5) $y > 6x + 2$

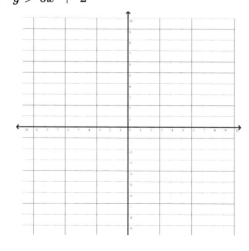

6) $y < x + 1$

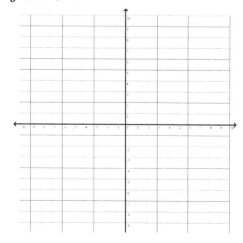

✏️▶ **Sketch the graph of each linear inequality.**

1) $y < -5x + 1$

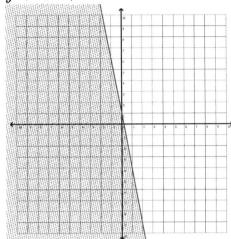

2) $y < 6x$

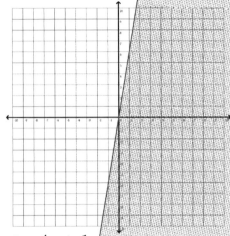

3) $y > x + 2$

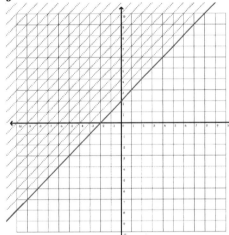

4) $y > -4x + 1$

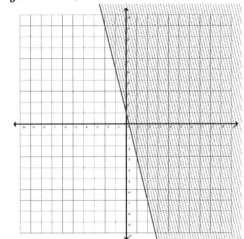

5) $y > 6x + 2$

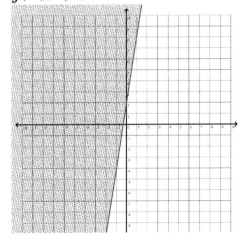

6) $y < x + 1$

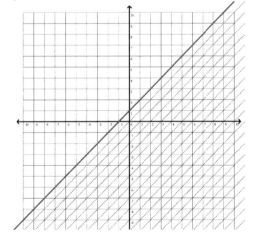

✏️▷ **Find the slope of the line through each pair of points.**

1) $(2, 6), (3, 8)$

2) $(0, 5), (5, 55)$

3) $(2, 1), (1, 13)$

4) $(0, 0), (-3, 30)$

5) $(6, 1), (5, 15)$

6) $(2, 2), (1, -7)$

7) $(3, 3), (8, -77)$

8) $(6, 6), (11, 41)$

9) $(6, 2), (9, 65)$

10) $(6, 0), (3, 21)$

11) $(4, 4), (2, 44)$

12) $(3, 3), (-1, 79)$

13) $(3, 3), (2, -2)$

14) $(5, 0), (8, -33)$

15) $(5, 4), (7, -4)$

16) $(5, 5), (1, 29)$

17) $(5, 3), (4, -11)$

18) $(2, 0), (1, 17)$

19) $(1, 3), (0, -14)$

20) $(1, 1), (0, 6)$

21) $(2, 7), (5, 43)$

22) $(4, 1), (3, 4)$

✏️▷ **Find the slope of the line through each pair of points.**

1) $(2, 6), (3, 8) \Rightarrow 2$

2) $(0, 5), (5, 55) \Rightarrow 10$

3) $(2, 1), (1, 13) \Rightarrow -12$

4) $(0, 0), (-3, 30) \Rightarrow -10$

5) $(6, 1), (5, 15) \Rightarrow -14$

6) $(2, 2), (1, -7) \Rightarrow 9$

7) $(3, 3), (8, -77) \Rightarrow -16$

8) $(6, 6), (11, 41) \Rightarrow 7$

9) $(6, 2), (9, 65) \Rightarrow 21$

10) $(6, 0), (3, 21) \Rightarrow -7$

11) $(4, 4), (2, 44) \Rightarrow -20$

12) $(3, 3), (-1, 79) \Rightarrow -19$

13) $(3, 3), (2, -2) \Rightarrow 5$

14) $(5, 0), (8, -33) \Rightarrow -11$

15) $(5, 4), (7, -4) \Rightarrow -4$

16) $(5, 5), (1, 29) \Rightarrow -6$

17) $(5, 3), (4, -11) \Rightarrow 14$

18) $(2, 0), (1, 17) \Rightarrow -17$

19) $(1, 3), (0, -14) \Rightarrow 17$

20) $(1, 1), (0, 6) \Rightarrow -5$

21) $(2, 7), (5, 43) \Rightarrow 12$

22) $(4, 1), (3, 4) \Rightarrow -3$

testinar.com/t/?c=9

✏️ **Find the midpoint of the line segment with the given endpoints.**

1) $(1, 2), (-7, -6)$

2) $(-8, -2), (4, -4)$

3) $(-6, 10), (4, -8)$

4) $(-4, 10), (2, -4)$

5) $(11, 1), (-7, 1)$

6) $(-6, -1), (4, -3)$

7) $(-5, 0), (5, 4)$

8) $(0, -10), (-4, 6)$

9) $(-13, 7), (7, -5)$

10) $(6, 2), (-8, -2)$

11) $(-3, -5), (1, 3)$

12) $(-9, 5), (3, 1)$

13) $(7, -6), (-7, 4)$

14) $(3, 1), (1, -5)$

15) $(-3, -5), (5, 3)$

16) $(-1, 9), (7, -7)$

17) $(6, -8), (0, 4)$

18) $(5, -1), (-1, -5)$

19) $(3, -3), (3, 7)$

20) $(-4, -3), (6, 7)$

21) $(-4, -5), (-2, 5)$

22) $(-5, -3), (5, -1)$

▷ **Find the midpoint of the line segment with the given endpoints.**

1) $(1, 2), (-7, -6) \Rightarrow M = (-3, -2)$ 2) $(-8, -2), (4, -4) \Rightarrow M = (-2, -3)$

3) $(-6, 10), (4, -8) \Rightarrow M = (-1, 1)$ 4) $(-4, 10), (2, -4) \Rightarrow M = (-1, 3)$

5) $(11, 1), (-7, 1) \Rightarrow M = (2, 1)$ 6) $(-6, -1), (4, -3) \Rightarrow M = (-1, -2)$

7) $(-5, 0), (5, 4) \Rightarrow M = (0, 2)$ 8) $(0, -10), (-4, 6) \Rightarrow M = (-2, -2)$

9) $(-13, 7), (7, -5) \Rightarrow M = (-3, 1)$ 10) $(6, 2), (-8, -2) \Rightarrow M = (-1, 0)$

11) $(-3, -5), (1, 3) \Rightarrow M = (-1, -1)$ 12) $(-9, 5), (3, 1) \Rightarrow M = (-3, 3)$

13) $(7, -6), (-7, 4) \Rightarrow M = (0, -1)$ 14) $(3, 1), (1, -5) \Rightarrow M = (2, -2)$

15) $(-3, -5), (5, 3) \Rightarrow M = (1, -1)$ 16) $(-1, 9), (7, -7) \Rightarrow M = (3, 1)$

17) $(6, -8), (0, 4) \Rightarrow M = (3, -2)$ 18) $(5, -1), (-1, -5) \Rightarrow M = (2, -3)$

19) $(3, -3), (3, 7) \Rightarrow M = (3, 2)$ 20) $(-4, -3), (6, 7) \Rightarrow M = (1, 2)$

21) $(-4, -5), (-2, 5) \Rightarrow M = (-3, 0)$ 22) $(-5, -3), (5, -1) \Rightarrow M = (0, -2)$

Find the distance between each pair of points.

1) $(-4, -3), (4, -6)$

2) $(6, 2), (-6, 2)$

3) $(1, 2), (4, -2)$

4) $(0, -4), (7, 4)$

5) $(1, -6), (-6, 6)$

6) $(-3, 2), (1, -2)$

7) $(-2, -3), (2, -3)$

8) $(-4, -1), (4, 6)$

9) $(8, 4), (-4, -4)$

10) $(1, 1), (7, 5)$

11) $(-3, 9), (3, -1)$

12) $(8, -9), (-8, 1)$

13) $(5, 5), (-5, -2)$

14) $(-3, -6), (7, 6)$

15) $(7, 3), (-3, -3)$

16) $(-10, -4), (7, 4)$

17) $(3, -5), (-3, -5)$

18) $(-2, -7), (6, 7)$

19) $(1, -3), (-4, 3)$

20) $(7, 0), (-7, 4)$

21) $(4, -10), (-4, 5)$

22) $(-1, 1), (1, -4)$

✏️ **Find the distance between each pair of points.**

1) $(-4, -3), (4, -6) \Rightarrow D = 9$

2) $(6, 2), (-6, 2) \Rightarrow D = 4$

3) $(1, 2), (4, -2) \Rightarrow D = 5$

4) $(0, -4), (7, 4) \Rightarrow D = 7$

5) $(1, -6), (-6, 6) \Rightarrow D = 5$

6) $(-3, 2), (1, -2) \Rightarrow D = 2$

7) $(-2, -3), (2, -3) \Rightarrow D = 6$

8) $(-4, -1), (4, 6) \Rightarrow D = 5$

9) $(8, 4), (-4, -4) \Rightarrow D = 4$

10) $(1, 1), (7, 5) \Rightarrow D = 10$

11) $(-3, 9), (3, -1) \Rightarrow D = 8$

12) $(8, -9), (-8, 1) \Rightarrow D = 8$

13) $(5, 5), (-5, -2) \Rightarrow D = 3$

14) $(-3, -6), (7, 6) \Rightarrow D = 4$

15) $(7, 3), (-3, -3) \Rightarrow D = 4$

16) $(-10, -4), (7, 4) \Rightarrow D = 3$

17) $(3, -5), (-3, -5) \Rightarrow D = 10$

18) $(-2, -7), (6, 7) \Rightarrow D = 4$

19) $(1, -3), (-4, 3) \Rightarrow D = 3$

20) $(7, 0), (-7, 4) \Rightarrow D = 4$

21) $(4, -10), (-4, 5) \Rightarrow D = 5$

22) $(-1, 1), (1, -4) \Rightarrow D = 3$

✏️ **Write each polynomial in standard form.**

1) $-6x^2 - x + 10x^3 =$

2) $-2(4x^3 - x) - 7x^4 =$

3) $-14x^2 - x + 18x^3 =$

4) $15x^2 - 16x^3 =$

5) $-13x^2 - 6 + 15x^3 =$

6) $x - 2(22x^3 - x) - 26x^4 =$

7) $-15x^2 - 5 + 18x^3 =$

8) $-2(19x^3 - x) - 23x^4 =$

9) $-22x^2 - x + 24x^3 =$

10) $8x^2 - 10x^3 =$

11) $-2(15x^3 - x) - 16x^4 =$

12) $-14x^2 - 6 + 17x^3 =$

13) $x - 2(8x^3 - x) - 12x^4 =$

➤ **Write each polynomial in standard form.**

1) $-6x^2 - x + 10x^3 = 10x^3 - 6x^2 - x$

2) $-2(4x^3 - x) - 7x^4 = -7x^4 - 8x^3 + 2x$

3) $-14x^2 - x + 18x^3 = 18x^3 - 14x^2 - x$

4) $15x^2 - 16x^3 = -16x^3 + 15x^2$

5) $-13x^2 - 6 + 15x^3 = 15x^3 - 13x^2 - 6$

6) $x - 2(22x^3 - x) - 26x^4 = -26x^4 - 44x^3 + 3x$

7) $-15x^2 - 5 + 18x^3 = 18x^3 - 15x^2 - 5$

8) $-2(19x^3 - x) - 23x^4 = -23x^4 - 38x^3 + 2x$

9) $-22x^2 - x + 24x^3 = 24x^3 - 22x^2 - x$

10) $8x^2 - 10x^3 = -10x^3 + 8x^2$

11) $-2(15x^3 - x) - 16x^4 = -16x^4 - 30x^3 + 2x$

12) $-14x^2 - 6 + 17x^3 = 17x^3 - 14x^2 - 6$

13) $x - 2(8x^3 - x) - 12x^4 = -12x^4 - 16x^3 + 3x$

✏️ **Simplify each expression.**

1) $3x(x + 5x^2 - 2x^4) =$

2) $18 + 3(-2x^3 - 4x^2) - 2 + x =$

3) $13x(x + 2x^2 - 5x^4) =$

4) $20 + 5x^3 - 3x^2 - 2 =$

5) $(-x + 3x^2)x =$

6) $(-x + 21x^2)x =$

7) $(x - 12x^2)(x + 3) =$

8) $(x - 9x^2)(x + 3) =$

9) $2x(x + 7x^2 - 3x^4) =$

10) $11 + 3(-3x^3 - 2x^2) - 4 + x =$

11) $(-x + 11x^2)x =$

12) $19 + 3(-2x^3 - 2x^2) - 2 + x =$

13) $15x(x + 2x^2 - 7x^4) =$

✎ **Simplify each expression.**

1) $3x(x + 5x^2 - 2x^4) = -6x^4 + 15x^3 + 3x^2$

2) $18 + 3(-2x^3 - 4x^2) - 2 + x = -6x^3 - 12x^2 + x + 16$

3) $13x(x + 2x^2 - 5x^4) = -65x^4 + 26x^3 + 13x^2$

4) $20 + 5x^3 - 3x^2 - 2 = 5x^3 - 3x^2 + 18$

5) $(-x + 3x^2)x = 3x^3 - x^2$

6) $(-x + 21x^2)x = 21x^3 - x^2$

7) $(x - 12x^2)(x + 3) = -12x^3 - 35x^2 + 3x$

8) $(x - 9x^2)(x + 3) = -9x^3 - 26x^2 + 3x$

9) $2x(x + 7x^2 - 3x^4) = -6x^4 + 14x^3 + 2x^2$

10) $11 + 3(-3x^3 - 2x^2) - 4 + x = -9x^3 - 6x^2 + x + 7$

11) $(-x + 11x^2)x = 11x^3 - x^2$

12) $19 + 3(-2x^3 - 2x^2) - 2 + x = -6x^3 - 6x^2 + x + 17$

13) $15x(x + 2x^2 - 7x^4) = -105x^4 + 30x^3 + 15x^2$

testinar.com/t/?c=10

✏️ **Simplify each expression.**

1) $(-5x + 4) + (3x - 2) =$

2) $(-6x^2 + 7x) - (7x^2 + 5x) =$

3) $(9x + 6) - (4x + 4) =$

4) $(2x^2 + 7x) - (2x^2 + 3x) =$

5) $(7x^2 + 6x) + (3x^2 - 4x) =$

6) $(-8x + 6) + (4x - 4) =$

7) $(6x^2 + 3x) + (4x^2 - 2x) =$

8) $(9x^2 + 6x) - (7x^2 + 4x) =$

9) $(5x^2 + 8x) + (3x^2 - 6x) =$

10) $(-2x^2 + 7x) - (2x^2 + 5x) =$

11) $(-4x + 6) + (2x - 4) =$

12) $(-3x + 5) + (2x - 3) =$

13) $(5x^2 + 9x) - (3x^2 + 7x) =$

✏️▷ **Simplify each expression.**

1) $(-5x + 4) + (3x - 2) = -2x + 2$

2) $(-6x^2 + 7x) - (7x^2 + 5x) = -13x^2 + 2x$

3) $(9x + 6) - (4x + 4) = 5x + 2$

4) $(2x^2 + 7x) - (2x^2 + 3x) = 0x^2 + 4x$

5) $(7x^2 + 6x) + (3x^2 - 4x) = 10x^2 + 2x$

6) $(-8x + 6) + (4x - 4) = -4x + 2$

7) $(6x^2 + 3x) + (4x^2 - 2x) = 10x^2 + 1x$

8) $(9x^2 + 6x) - (7x^2 + 4x) = 2x^2 + 2x$

9) $(5x^2 + 8x) + (3x^2 - 6x) = 8x^2 + 2x$

10) $(-2x^2 + 7x) - (2x^2 + 5x) = -4x^2 + 2x$

11) $(-4x + 6) + (2x - 4) = -2x + 2$

12) $(-3x + 5) + (2x - 3) = -1x + 2$

13) $(5x^2 + 9x) - (3x^2 + 7x) = 2x^2 + 2x$

120

✏️ **Simplify each expression.**

testinar.com/t/?c=10

1) $-9x^2y^3z \times 5x =$

2) $9xy \times 4x^2y =$

3) $-4xy \times (-2z) =$

4) $8x^2y^3z \times 5x =$

5) $5x^2y^3z \times 4x =$

6) $2x^2y^2z \times 2xz^2 =$

7) $-5xy \times (-3z) =$

8) $-8x^2y^2z \times 7xz^2 =$

9) $9x^2y^2z \times 5xz^2 =$

10) $5xy \times 2x^2y =$

11) $-6x^2y^2z \times 7xz^2 =$

12) $2xy \times 4x^2y =$

13) $-3x^2y^2z \times 4xz^2 =$

14) $7xy \times 2x^2y =$

15) $-1xy \times 3x^2y =$

16) $-10x^2y^2z \times 4xz^2 =$

17) $-8xy \times (-3z) =$

18) $2x^2y^3z \times 3x =$

19) $-5xy \times 4x^2y =$

20) $-5x^2y^2z \times 5xz^2 =$

21) $8x^2y^2z \times 7xz^2 =$

22) $3x^2y^3z \times 3x =$

✏️ **Simplify each expression.**

1) $-9x^2y^3z \times 5x = -45x^3y^3z$

2) $9xy \times 4x^2y = 36x^3y^2$

3) $-4xy \times (-2z) = 8xyz$

4) $8x^2y^3z \times 5x = 40x^3y^3z$

5) $5x^2y^3z \times 4x = 20x^3y^3z$

6) $2x^2y^2z \times 2xz^2 = 4x^3y^2z^3$

7) $-5xy \times (-3z) = 15xyz$

8) $-8x^2y^2z \times 7xz^2 = -56x^3y^2z^3$

9) $9x^2y^2z \times 5xz^2 = 45x^3y^2z^3$

10) $5xy \times 2x^2y = 10x^3y^2$

11) $-6x^2y^2z \times 7xz^2 = -42x^3y^2z^3$

12) $2xy \times 4x^2y = 8x^3y^2$

13) $-3x^2y^2z \times 4xz^2 = -12x^3y^2z^3$

14) $7xy \times 2x^2y = 14x^3y^2$

15) $-1xy \times 3x^2y = -3x^3y^2$

16) $-10x^2y^2z \times 4xz^2 = -40x^3y^2z^3$

17) $-8xy \times (-3z) = 24xyz$

18) $2x^2y^3z \times 3x = 6x^3y^3z$

19) $-5xy \times 4x^2y = -20x^3y^2$

20) $-5x^2y^2z \times 5xz^2 = -25x^3y^2z^3$

21) $8x^2y^2z \times 7xz^2 = 56x^3y^2z^3$

22) $3x^2y^3z \times 3x = 9x^3y^3z$

✏️▷ **Find the equation of the line passing through the given points.**

1) $(-9x - 4)(-1x + 4) =$

2) $(-8x - 3)(-3x + 2) =$

3) $(-10x - 10)(3x + 5) =$

4) $(-6x - 1)(3x + 1) =$

5) $(-3x - 10)(-4x + 1) =$

6) $(-9x - 7)(1x + 1) =$

7) $(-8x - 8)(-5x + 5) =$

8) $(-1x - 4)(1x + 5) =$

9) $(-10x - 5)(-3x + 5) =$

10) $(-9x - 2)(-4x + 5) =$

11) $(-7x - 3)(5x + 5) =$

12) $(-5x - 2)(-1x + 5) =$

13) $(-9x - 3)(-3x + 3) =$

✏️ **Find the equation of the line passing through the given points.**

1) $(-9x - 4)(-1x + 4) = 9x^2 - 32x - 16$

2) $(-8x - 3)(-3x + 2) = 24x^2 - 7x - 6$

3) $(-10x - 10)(3x + 5) = -30x^2 - 80x - 50$

4) $(-6x - 1)(3x + 1) = -18x^2 - 9x - 1$

5) $(-3x - 10)(-4x + 1) = 12x^2 + 37x - 10$

6) $(-9x - 7)(1x + 1) = -9x^2 - 16x - 7$

7) $(-8x - 8)(-5x + 5) = 40x^2 x - 40$

8) $(-1x - 4)(1x + 5) = -1x^2 - 9x - 20$

9) $(-10x - 5)(-3x + 5) = 30x^2 - 35x - 25$

10) $(-9x - 2)(-4x + 5) = 36x^2 - 37x - 10$

11) $(-7x - 3)(5x + 5) = -35x^2 - 50x - 15$

12) $(-5x - 2)(-1x + 5) = 5x^2 - 23x - 10$

13) $(-9x - 3)(-3x + 3) = 27x^2 - 18x - 9$

Factor each trinomial.

testinar.com/t/?c=10

1) $x^2 - 121 =$

2) $x^2 - 7x - 18 =$

3) $x^2 + 5x - 36 =$

4) $x^2 - 6x - 16 =$

5) $x^2 + 13x + 36 =$

6) $-12x^2 - 26x - 12 =$

7) $x^2 - 6x + 5 =$

8) $x^2 + 10x + 25 =$

9) $x^2 - 1x - 20 =$

10) $x^2 - 6x + 5 =$

11) $x^2 + 4x - 45 =$

12) $x^2 - 5x - 14 =$

13) $2x^2 + 3x - 5 =$

14) $x^2 + 8x + 15 =$

15) $x^2 - 64 =$

16) $x^2 - 2x - 15 =$

17) $x^2 - 2x - 15 =$

18) $-10x^2 - 24x - 8 =$

19) $x^2 - 9x + 18 =$

20) $x^2 - 4x - 5 =$

21) $x^2 - 11x + 18 =$

22) $x^2 - 9x + 14 =$

✎ **Factor each trinomial.**

1) $x^2 - 121 = (x + 11)(x - 11)$

2) $x^2 - 7x - 18 =$
$(x - 9)(x + 2)$

3) $x^2 + 5x - 36 =$
$(x - 4)(x + 9)$

4) $x^2 - 6x - 16 =$
$(x + 2)(x - 8)$

5) $x^2 + 13x + 36 =$
$(x + 4)(x + 9)$

6) $-12x^2 - 26x - 12 =$
$(-4x - 6)(3x + 2)$

7) $x^2 - 6x + 5 = (x - 1)(x - 5)$

8) $x^2 + 10x + 25 =$
$(x + 5)(x + 5)$

9) $x^2 - 1x - 20 =$
$(x - 5)(x + 4)$

10) $x^2 - 6x + 5 = (x - 5)(x - 1)$

11) $x^2 + 4x - 45 =$
$(x - 5)(x + 9)$

12) $x^2 - 5x - 14 =$
$(x - 7)(x + 2)$

13) $2x^2 + 3x - 5 =$
$(-2x - 5)(-x + 1)$

14) $x^2 + 8x + 15 =$
$(x + 3)(x + 5)$

15) $x^2 - 64 = (x - 8)(x + 8)$

16) $x^2 - 2x - 15 =$
$(x - 5)(x + 3)$

17) $x^2 - 2x - 15 =$
$(x + 3)(x - 5)$

18) $-10x^2 - 24x - 8 =$
$(-10x - 4)(x + 2)$

19) $x^2 - 9x + 18 =$
$(x - 6)(x - 3)$

20) $x^2 - 4x - 5 = (x - 5)(x + 1)$

21) $x^2 - 11x + 18 =$
$(x - 9)(x - 2)$

22) $x^2 - 9x + 14 =$
$(x - 7)(x - 2)$

✏️ **Simplify each expression.**

testinar.com/t/?c=10

1) $4x^2y^3 \div 2y =$

2) $\frac{-28x^2y^3z}{4yz} =$

3) $\frac{27xzy}{-3yz} =$

4) $-30xz^2 \div 3xz^2 =$

5) $\frac{-12x^2y^3z}{2yz} =$

6) $-24x^2y^3 \div 3y =$

7) $\frac{-14xzy}{-2yz} =$

8) $-8xz^2 \div 4xz^2 =$

9) $\frac{-9xzy}{-3yz} =$

10) $-8xz^2 \div 2xz^2 =$

11) $6xz^2 \div 3xz^2 =$

12) $\frac{-8x^2y^3z}{2yz} =$

13) $\frac{-24xzy}{-4yz} =$

14) $\frac{32x^2y^3z}{4yz} =$

15) $-32xz^2 \div 4xz^2 =$

16) $-8x^2y^3 \div 4y =$

17) $24xz^2 \div 4xz^2 =$

18) $\frac{14xzy}{-2yz} =$

19) $-9xz^2 \div 3xz^2 =$

20) $12xz^2 \div 3xz^2 =$

21) $27xz^2 \div 3xz^2 =$

22) $\frac{-16x^2y^3z}{2yz} =$

✏️ **Simplify each expression.**

1) $4x^2y^3 \div 2y = 2x^2y^2$

2) $\frac{-28x^2y^3z}{4yz} = -7x^2y^2$

3) $\frac{27xzy}{-3yz} = -9x$

4) $-30xz^2 \div 3xz^2 = -10$

5) $\frac{-12x^2y^3z}{2yz} = -6x^2y^2$

6) $-24x^2y^3 \div 3y = -8x^2y^2$

7) $\frac{-14xzy}{-2yz} = 7x$

8) $-8xz^2 \div 4xz^2 = -2$

9) $\frac{-9xzy}{-3yz} = 3x$

10) $-8xz^2 \div 2xz^2 = -4$

11) $6xz^2 \div 3xz^2 = 2$

12) $\frac{-8x^2y^3z}{2yz} = -4x^2y^2$

13) $\frac{-24xzy}{-4yz} = 6x$

14) $\frac{32x^2y^3z}{4yz} = 8x^2y^2$

15) $-32xz^2 \div 4xz^2 = -8$

16) $-8x^2y^3 \div 4y = -2x^2y^2$

17) $24xz^2 \div 4xz^2 = 6$

18) $\frac{14xzy}{-2yz} = -7x$

19) $-9xz^2 \div 3xz^2 = -3$

20) $12xz^2 \div 3xz^2 = 4$

21) $27xz^2 \div 3xz^2 = 9$

22) $\frac{-16x^2y^3z}{2yz} = -8x^2y^2$

✏️ **Write each number in scientific notation.**

1) $0.748 =$

2) $0.029 =$

3) $0.581 =$

4) $848,000,000 =$

5) $887,000,000 =$

6) $0.000366 =$

7) $43,900,000 =$

8) $0.0236 =$

9) $651,000,000 =$

10) $0.0869 =$

11) $436,000,000 =$

12) $569,000 =$

13) $845,000,000 =$

14) $381,000 =$

15) $77,800,000 =$

16) $0.0733 =$

17) $0.878 =$

18) $0.000363 =$

19) $46,000,000 =$

20) $0.00345 =$

21) $757,000 =$

22) $484,000 =$

Write each number in scientific notation.

1) $0.748 = 7.48 \times 10^{-1}$

2) $0.029 = 2.9 \times 10^{-2}$

3) $0.581 = 5.81 \times 10^{-1}$

4) $848,000,000 = 8.48 \times 10^{8}$

5) $887,000,000 = 8.87 \times 10^{8}$

6) $0.000366 = 3.66 \times 10^{-4}$

7) $43,900,000 = 4.39 \times 10^{7}$

8) $0.0236 = 2.36 \times 10^{-2}$

9) $651,000,000 = 6.51 \times 10^{8}$

10) $0.0869 = 8.69 \times 10^{-2}$

11) $436,000,000 = 4.36 \times 10^{8}$

12) $569,000 = 5.69 \times 10^{5}$

13) $845,000,000 = 8.45 \times 10^{8}$

14) $381,000 = 3.81 \times 10^{5}$

15) $77,800,000 = 7.78 \times 10^{7}$

16) $0.0733 = 7.33 \times 10^{-2}$

17) $0.878 = 8.78 \times 10^{-1}$

18) $0.000363 = 3.63 \times 10^{-4}$

19) $46,000,000 = 4.6 \times 10^{7}$

20) $0.00345 = 3.45 \times 10^{-3}$

21) $757,000 = 7.57 \times 10^{5}$

22) $484,000 = 4.84 \times 10^{5}$

✏️ **Find Mean, Median, Mode, and Range of the Given Data.**

1) $10, 24, 17, 3, 6, 56, 6$

2) $2, 54, 13, 24, 17, 6, 6$

3) $15, 7, 10, 7, 2, 31, 20$

4) $10, 20, 16, 4, 5, 26, 5$

5) $3, 57, 10, 21, 17, 5, 5$

6) $13, 21, 19, 3, 8, 62, 8$

7) $16, 7, 10, 7, 3, 49, 20$

8) $12, 21, 18, 1, 8, 32, 8$

9) $1, 63, 11, 21, 16, 5, 5$

10) $16, 6, 13, 6, 1, 43, 20$

11) $12, 22, 19, 3, 5, 29, 5$

12) $14, 21, 17, 2, 9, 38, 9$

13) $16, 5, 10, 5, 1, 37, 20$

✏️ **Find Mean, Median, Mode, and Range of the Given Data.**

1) $10, 24, 17, 3, 6, 56, 6 \Rightarrow$ mean: 17.43, median: 10, mode: 6, range : 21

2) $2, 54, 13, 24, 17, 6, 6 \Rightarrow$ mean: 17.43, median: 13, mode: 6, range : 22

3) $15, 7, 10, 7, 2, 31, 20 \Rightarrow$ mean: 13.14, median: 10, mode: 7, range : 18

4) $10, 20, 16, 4, 5, 26, 5 \Rightarrow$ mean: 12.29, median: 10, mode: 5, range : 16

5) $3, 57, 10, 21, 17, 5, 5 \Rightarrow$ mean: 16.86, median: 10, mode: 5, range : 18

6) $13, 21, 19, 3, 8, 62, 8 \Rightarrow$ mean: 19.14, median: 13, mode: 8, range : 18

7) $16, 7, 10, 7, 3, 49, 20 \Rightarrow$ mean: 16, median: 10, mode: 7, range : 17

8) $12, 21, 18, 1, 8, 32, 8 \Rightarrow$ mean: 14.29, median: 12, mode: 8, range : 20

9) $1, 63, 11, 21, 16, 5, 5 \Rightarrow$ mean: 17.43, median: 11, mode: 5, range : 20

10) $16, 6, 13, 6, 1, 43, 20 \Rightarrow$ mean: 15, median: 13, mode: 6, range : 19

11) $12, 22, 19, 3, 5, 29, 5 \Rightarrow$ mean: 13.57, median: 12, mode: 5, range : 19

12) $14, 21, 17, 2, 9, 38, 9 \Rightarrow$ mean: 15.71, median: 14, mode: 9, range : 19

13) $16, 5, 10, 5, 1, 37, 20 \Rightarrow$ mean: 13.43, median: 10, mode: 5, range : 19

✏️ **Pie Graph**

1) What percentage of pie graph is yellow?

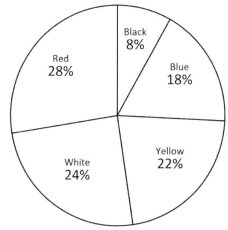

Black 8%
Blue 18%
Red 28%
Yellow 22%
White 24%

2) Which color is the most?

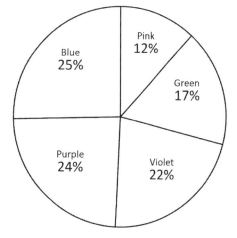

Pink 12%
Blue 25%
Green 17%
Purple 24%
Violet 22%

3) Which color is the least?

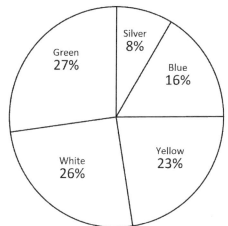

Silver 8%
Green 27%
Blue 16%
White 26%
Yellow 23%

4) What percent of people voted for Sepehr?

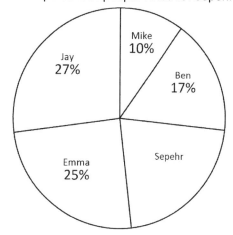

Mike 10%
Jay 27%
Ben 17%
Emma 25%
Sepehr

5) Which color is the most?

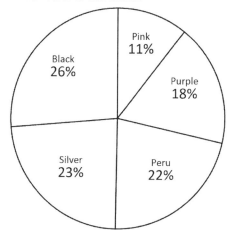

Pink 11%
Black 26%
Purple 18%
Silver 23%
Peru 22%

6) What percentage of pie graph is black?

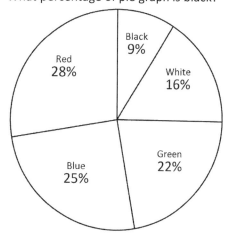

Black 9%
Red 28%
White 16%
Blue 25%
Green 22%

⬡ **Pie Graph**

1) What percentage of pie graph is yellow? 22%

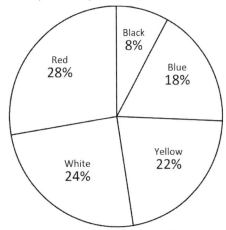

2) Which color is the most? **Blue**

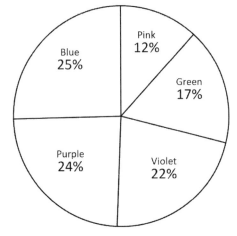

3) Which color is the least? **Silver**

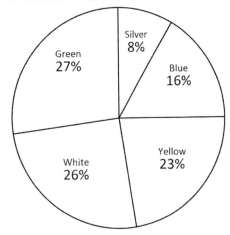

4) What percent of people voted for Sepehr? 21%

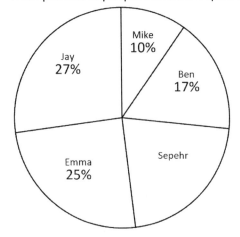

5) Which color is the most? **Black**

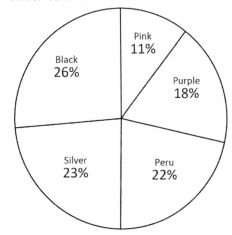

6) What percentage of pie graph is black? 9%

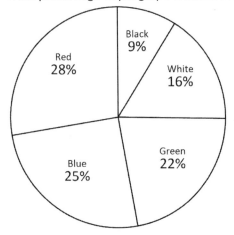

testinar.com/t/?c=13

 Solve.

1) A number is chosen at random from 1 to 13. Find the probability of selecting a 6 or smaller.

2) A number is chosen at random from 1 to 26. Find the probability of selecting a 6 or smaller.

3) A number is chosen at random from 1 to 15. Find the probability of selecting a 2 or smaller.

4) Bag A contains 22 red marbles and 6 green marbles. Bag B contains 5 black marbles and 9 orange marbles. What is the probability of selecting a green marble at random from bag A? What is the probability of selecting a black marble at random from Bag B?

5) A number is chosen at random from 1 to 44. Find the probability of selecting prime numbers.

6) Bag A contains 8 red marbles and 9 green marbles. Bag B contains 9 black marbles and 1 orange marbles. What is the probability of selecting a green marble at random from bag A? What is the probability of selecting a black marble at random from Bag B?

7) A number is chosen at random from 1 to 38. Find the probability of selecting prime numbers.

8) A number is chosen at random from 1 to 20. Find the probability of selecting prime numbers.

9) A number is chosen at random from 1 to 34. Find the probability of selecting prime numbers.

10) A number is chosen at random from 1 to 30. Find the probability of selecting prime numbers.

➦ **Solve.**

1) A number is chosen at random from 1 to 13. Find the probability of selecting a 6 or smaller.
$\frac{6}{13}$

2) A number is chosen at random from 1 to 26. Find the probability of selecting a 6 or smaller.
$\frac{3}{13}$

3) A number is chosen at random from 1 to 15. Find the probability of selecting a 2 or smaller.
$\frac{2}{15}$

4) Bag A contains 22 red marbles and 6 green marbles. Bag B contains 5 black marbles and 9 orange marbles. What is the probability of selecting a green marble at random from bag A? What is the probability of selecting a black marble at random from Bag B? $\frac{3}{14}, \frac{5}{14}$

5) A number is chosen at random from 1 to 44. Find the probability of selecting prime numbers. $\frac{7}{22}$

6) Bag A contains 8 red marbles and 9 green marbles. Bag B contains 9 black marbles and 1 orange marbles. What is the probability of selecting a green marble at random from bag A? What is the probability of selecting a black marble at random from Bag B? $\frac{9}{17}, \frac{9}{10}$

7) A number is chosen at random from 1 to 38. Find the probability of selecting prime numbers. $\frac{6}{19}$

8) A number is chosen at random from 1 to 20. Find the probability of selecting prime numbers. $\frac{2}{5}$

9) A number is chosen at random from 1 to 34. Find the probability of selecting prime numbers. $\frac{11}{34}$

10) A number is chosen at random from 1 to 30. Find the probability of selecting prime numbers. $\frac{1}{3}$

testinar.com/t/?c=14

✏️ **Find each missing length.**

1) $x =$

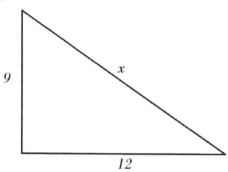

9

x

12

2) $x =$

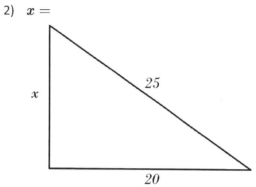

25

x

20

3) $x =$

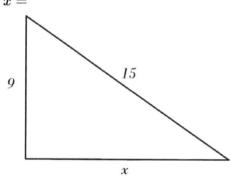

9

15

x

4) $x =$

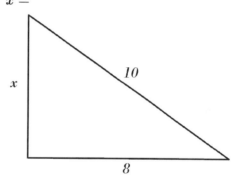

10

x

8

5) $x =$

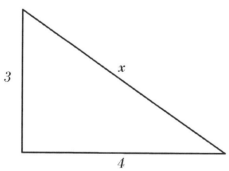

3

x

4

6) $x =$

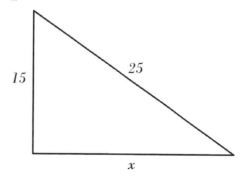

15

25

x

✏️ **Find each missing length.**

1) $x = 15$

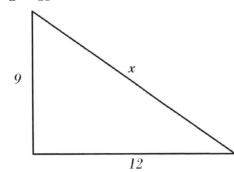

2) $x = 15$

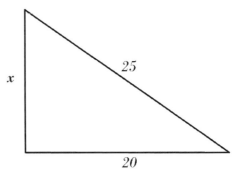

3) $x = 12$

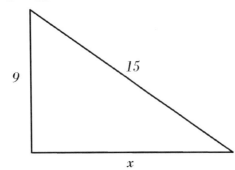

4) $x = 6$

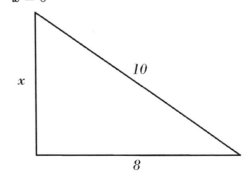

5) $x = 5$

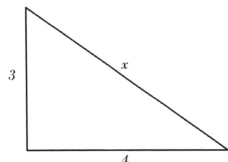

6) $x = 20$

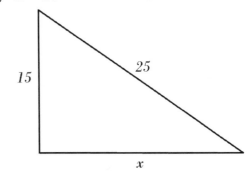

✏️➤ **Find the area of each.**

1) What is the area of the triangle?

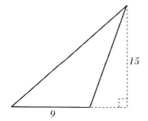

2) What is the area of the triangle?

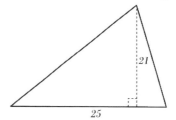

3) What is the area of the triangle?

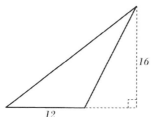

4) What is the area of the triangle?

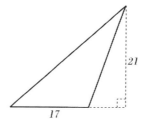

➤ **Find the measure of the unknown angle in each triangle.**

1) What is the unknown angle (α)?

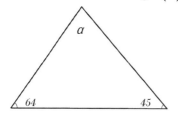

2) What is the unknown angle (α)?

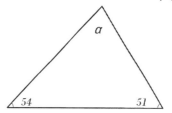

3) What is the unknown angle (α)?

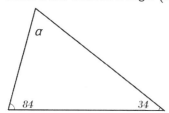

4) What is the unknown angle (α)?

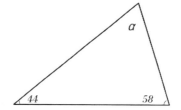

139

▱▷ **Find the area of each.**

1) $x = 67.5\,\text{m}^2$

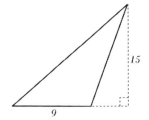

2) $x = 262.5\,\text{m}^2$

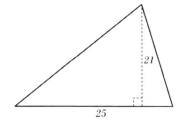

3) $x = 96\,\text{m}^2$

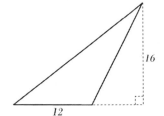

4) $x = 178.5\,\text{m}^2$

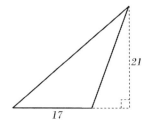

▱▷ **Find the measure of the unknown angle in each triangle.**

1) $\alpha = 71$

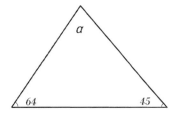

2) $\alpha = 75$

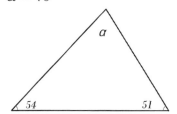

3) $\alpha = 62$

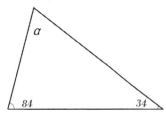

4) $\alpha = 78$

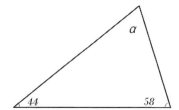

✏️ **Find the perimeter of each shape.**

1) What is the perimeter of the following regular hexagon?

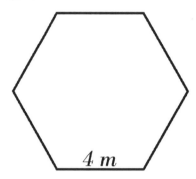

4 m

2) What is the perimeter of the following equilateral triangle?

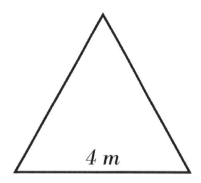

4 m

3) What is the perimeter of the following regular hexagon?

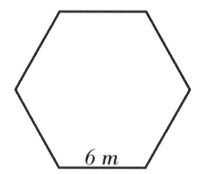

6 m

4) What is the perimeter of the following rectangle?

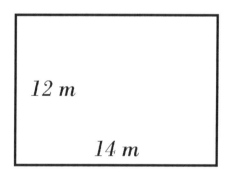

12 m

14 m

5) What is the perimeter of the following regular hexagon?

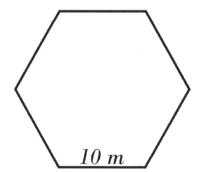

10 m

6) What is the perimeter of the following rectangle?

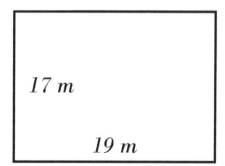

17 m

19 m

Find the perimeter of each shape.

1) What is the perimeter of the following regular hexagon? 24 *m*

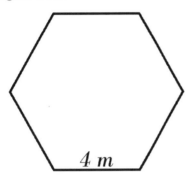

4 *m*

2) What is the perimeter of the following equilateral triangle? 12 *m*

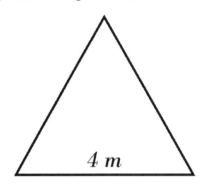

4 *m*

3) What is the perimeter of the following regular hexagon? 36 *m*

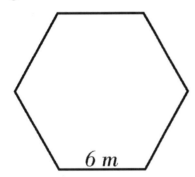

6 *m*

4) What is the perimeter of the following rectangle? 52 *m*

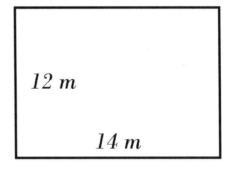

12 *m*

14 *m*

5) What is the perimeter of the following regular hexagon? 60 *m*

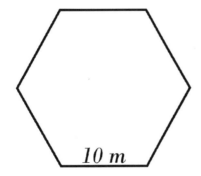

10 *m*

6) What is the perimeter of the following rectangle? 72 *m*

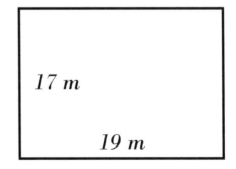

17 *m*

19 *m*

142

Area and Circumference of Circles

Find the area and circumference of each.

1)

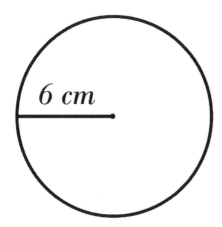

6 cm

2)

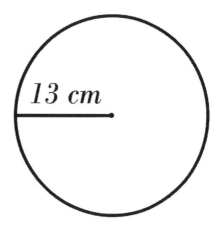

13 cm

3)

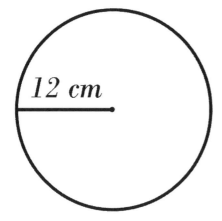

12 cm

4)

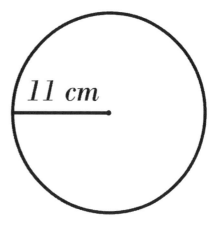

11 cm

5)

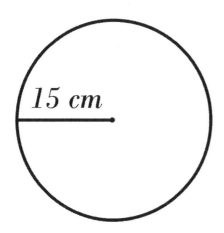

15 cm

6)

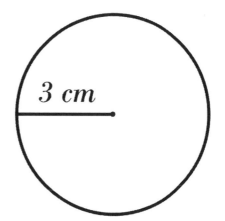

3 cm

▱ **Find the area and circumference of each.**

1) Area: 113.04 cm², Circumference: 37.68 cm

2) Area: 530.66 cm², Circumference: 81.64 cm

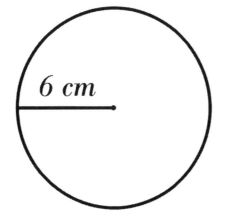
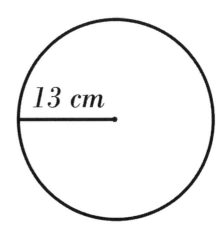

3) Area: 452.16 cm², Circumference: 75.36 cm

4) Area: 379.94 cm², Circumference: 69.08 cm

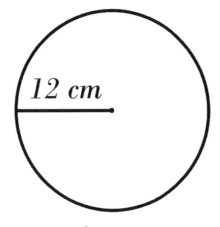
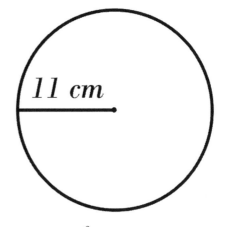

5) Area: 706.5 cm², Circumference: 94.2 cm

6) Area: 28.26 cm², Circumference: 18.84 cm

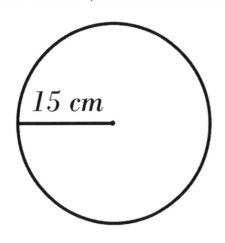
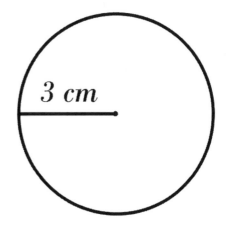

✏️ **Find the area of each.**

1)

13 cm

16 cm

2)

20 cm

23 cm

3)

17 cm

21 cm

4)

11 cm

5)

6 cm

6)

19 cm

23 cm

✏️ **Find the area of each.**

1) 208 cm^2

13 cm

16 cm

2) 460 cm^2

20 cm

23 cm

3) 357 cm^2

17 cm

21 cm

4) 121 cm^2

11 cm

5) 36 cm^2

6 cm

6) 437 cm^2

19 cm

23 cm

Find the area of each trapezoid.

1)

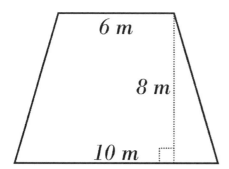

6 m

8 m

10 m

2)

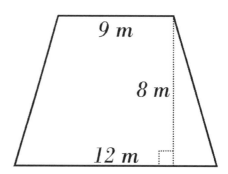

9 m

8 m

12 m

3)

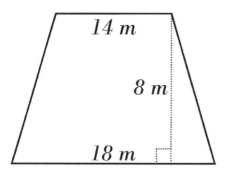

14 m

8 m

18 m

4)

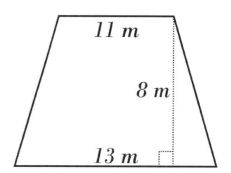

11 m

8 m

13 m

5)

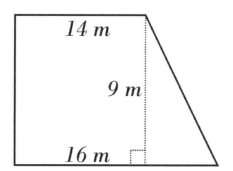

14 m

9 m

16 m

6)

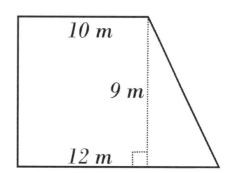

10 m

9 m

12 m

✏️ **Find the area of each trapezoid.**

1) $64 \, m^2$

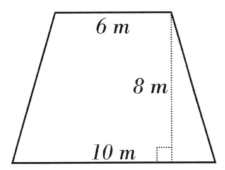

2) $84 \, m^2$

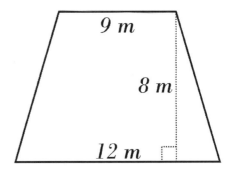

3) $128 \, m^2$

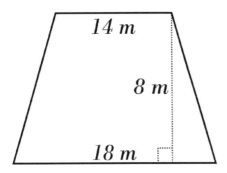

4) $96 \, m^2$

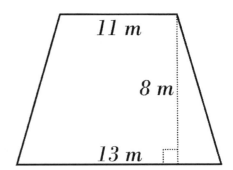

5) $135 \, m^2$

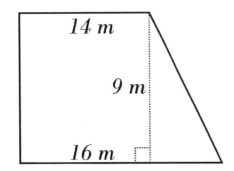

6) $99 \, m^2$

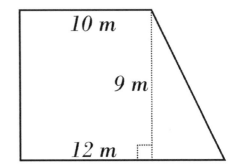

Find the value of x in the following figures.

1)

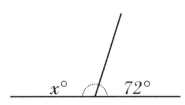

2)

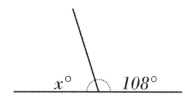

3)

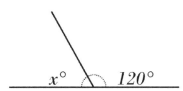

4)

5)

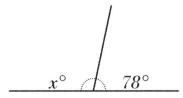

6)

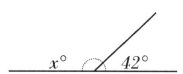

7)

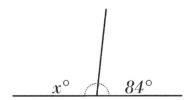

8)

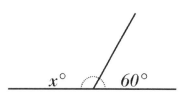

9)

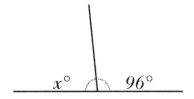

10)

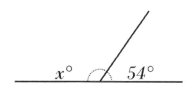

149

✏️ **Find the value of x in the following figures.**

1) 108°

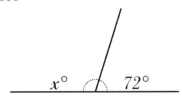

2) 72°

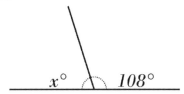

3) 60°

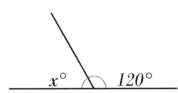

4) 114°

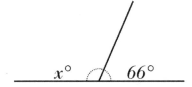

5) 102°

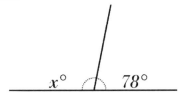

6) 138°

7) 96°

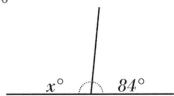

8) 120°

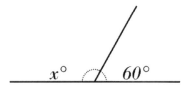

9) 84°

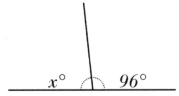

10) 126°

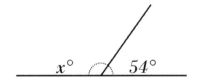

✏️ **Find the volume of each.**

1)

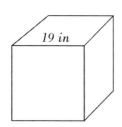

19 in

2)

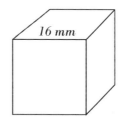

16 mm

3)

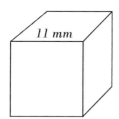

11 mm

4)

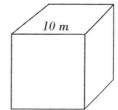

10 m

5)

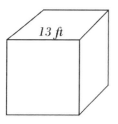

13 ft

6)

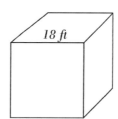

18 ft

7)

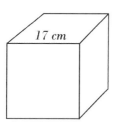

17 cm

8)

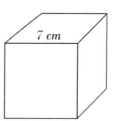

7 cm

9)

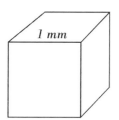

1 mm

10)

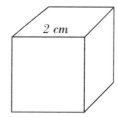

2 cm

Find the volume of each.

1) 6859 in³

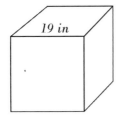
19 in

2) 4096 mm³

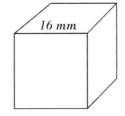
16 mm

3) 1331 mm³

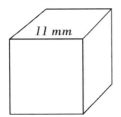
11 mm

4) 1000 m³

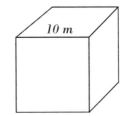
10 m

5) 2197 ft³

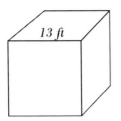
13 ft

6) 5832 ft³

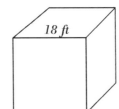
18 ft

7) 4913 cm³

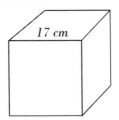
17 cm

8) 343 cm³

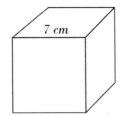
7 cm

9) 1 mm³

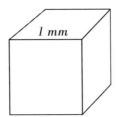
1 mm

10) 8 cm³

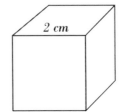
2 cm

✏️ **Find the volume of each rectangular prisms.**

1)

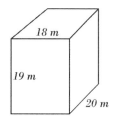

18 m
19 m
20 m

2)

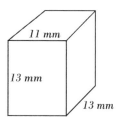

11 mm
13 mm
13 mm

3)

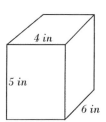

4 in
5 in
6 in

4)

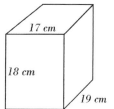

17 cm
18 cm
19 cm

5)

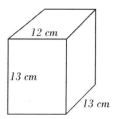

12 cm
13 cm
13 cm

6)

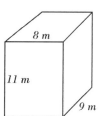

8 m
11 m
9 m

7)

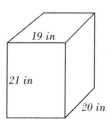

19 in
21 in
20 in

8)

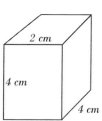

2 cm
4 cm
4 cm

9)

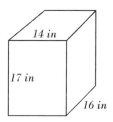

14 in
17 in
16 in

10)

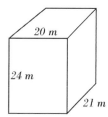

20 m
24 m
21 m

153

Find the volume of each rectangular prisms.

1) 6840 m³

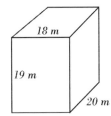

2) 1859 mm³

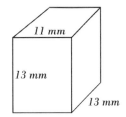

3) 120 in³

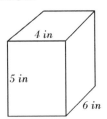

4) 5814 cm³

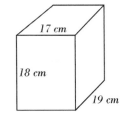

5) 2028 cm³

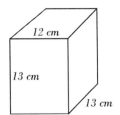

6) 792 m³

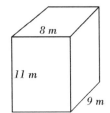

7) 7980 in³

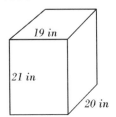

8) 32 cm³

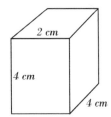

9) 3808 in³

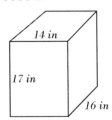

10) 10080 m³

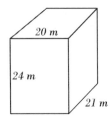

154

✏️ **Find the surface area of each cube.**

1)

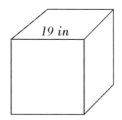

19 in

2)

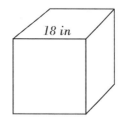

18 in

3)

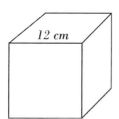

12 cm

4)

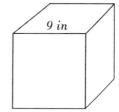

9 in

5)

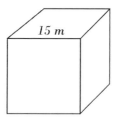

15 m

6)

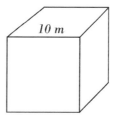

10 m

7)

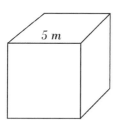

5 m

8)

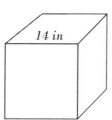

14 in

9)

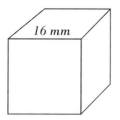

16 mm

10)

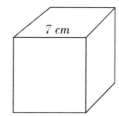

7 cm

Answers of volume and Surface Area of Cubes

 Find the surface area of each cube.

1) 2166 in²

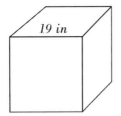
19 in

2) 1944 in²

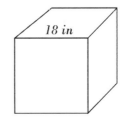
18 in

3) 864 cm²

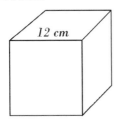
12 cm

4) 486 in²

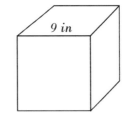
9 in

5) 1350 m²

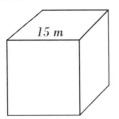
15 m

6) 600 m²

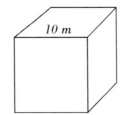
10 m

7) 150 m²

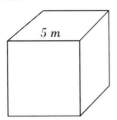
5 m

8) 1176 in²

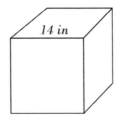
14 in

9) 1536 mm²

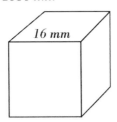
16 mm

10) 294 cm²

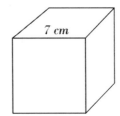
7 cm

Surface Area of a Rectangle Prism

✏️ **Find the surface area of each prism.**

1)

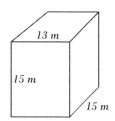

13 m
15 m
15 m

2)

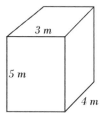

3 m
5 m
4 m

3)

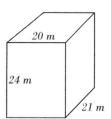

20 m
24 m
21 m

4)

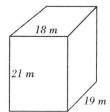

18 m
21 m
19 m

5)

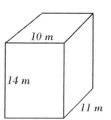

10 m
14 m
11 m

6)

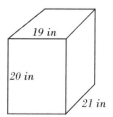

19 in
20 in
21 in

7)

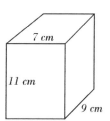

7 cm
11 cm
9 cm

8)

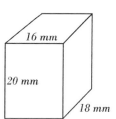

16 mm
20 mm
18 mm

9)

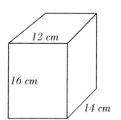

12 cm
16 cm
14 cm

10)

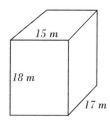

15 m
18 m
17 m

✏️ **Find the surface area of each prism.**

1) 1230 m²

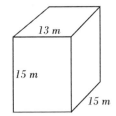

2) 94 m²

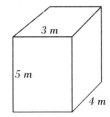

3) 2808 m²

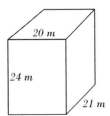

4) 2238 m²

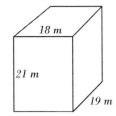

5) 808 m²

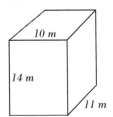

6) 2398 in²

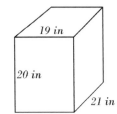

7) 478 cm²

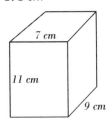

8) 1936 mm²

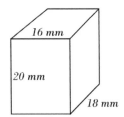

9) 1168 cm²

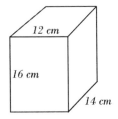

10) 1662 m²

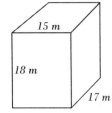

Volume of a Cylinder

✏️ **Find the volume of each cylinder.**

1)
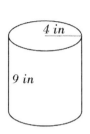
4 in
9 in

2)
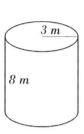
3 m
8 m

3)
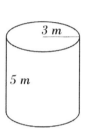
3 m
5 m

4)
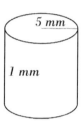
5 mm
1 mm

5)
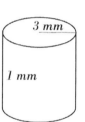
3 mm
1 mm

6)
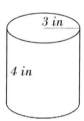
3 in
4 in

7)
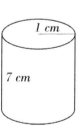
1 cm
7 cm

8)
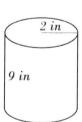
2 in
9 in

9)
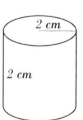
2 cm
2 cm

10)
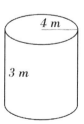
4 m
3 m

Find the volume of each cylinder.

1) 452.16 in³

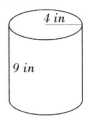

4 in

9 in

2) 226.08 m³

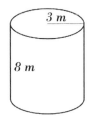

3 m

8 m

3) 141.3 m³

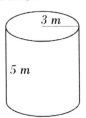

3 m

5 m

4) 78.5 mm³

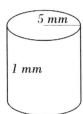

5 mm

1 mm

5) 28.26 mm³

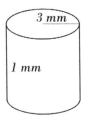

3 mm

1 mm

6) 113.04 in³

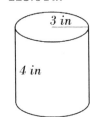

3 in

4 in

7) 21.98 cm³

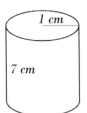

1 cm

7 cm

8) 113.04 in³

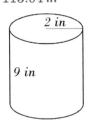

2 in

9 in

9) 25.12 cm³

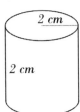

2 cm

2 cm

10) 150.72 m³

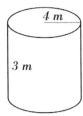

4 m

3 m

✏️ **Find the surface are of each cylinder.**

1)

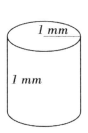

1 mm

1 mm

2)

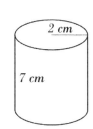

2 cm

7 cm

3)

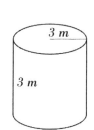

3 m

3 m

4)

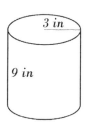

3 in

9 in

5)

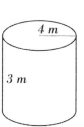

4 m

3 m

6)

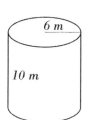

6 m

10 m

7)

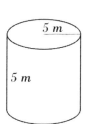

5 m

5 m

8)

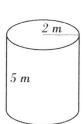

2 m

5 m

9)

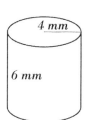

4 mm

6 mm

10)

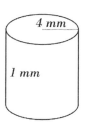

4 mm

1 mm

Find the surface are of each cylinder.

1) 12.56 mm²

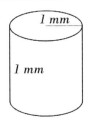

2) 113.04 cm²

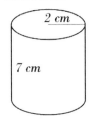

3) 113.04 m²

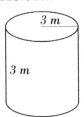

4) 226.08 in²

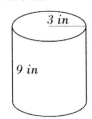

5) 175.84 m²

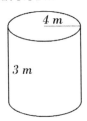

6) 602.88 m²

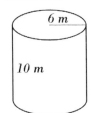

7) 314 m²

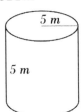

8) 87.92 m²

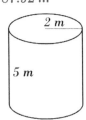

9) 251.2 mm²

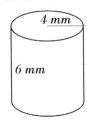

10) 125.6 mm²

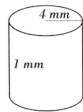

Evaluate each function.

1) $h(x) = 3x^2 + 5$, find $h(5)$

2) $h(x) = 3x^2 - x + 3$, find $h(9)$

3) $m(u) = 5u^2 + u + 7$, find $m(6)$

4) $h(x) = 8x^2 + 2$, find $h(1)$

5) $f(x) = 11x^2 - x + 2$, find $f(4)$

6) $f(x) = 11x^2 + 4$, find $f(1)$

7) $g(t) = 2t^2 - t + 2$, find $g(2)$

8) $h(x) = 8x^2 + x + 3$, find $h(8)$

9) $m(u) = 10u^2 + 2$, find $m(6)$

10) $h(x) = 3x^2 + x + 4$, find $h(1)$

11) $g(t) = 7t^2 + 1$, find $g(1)$

12) $m(u) = 10u^2 - u + 8$, find $m(6)$

13) $p(s) = 4s + 2$, find $p(8)$

14) $f(x) = 6x^2 - x + 8$, find $f(7)$

15) $p(s) = 9s + 8$, find $p(3)$

16) $g(t) = 7t^2 - t + 6$, find $g(2)$

17) $g(t) = 7t^2 + t + 7$, find $g(6)$

18) $f(x) = 6x + 7$, find $f(8)$

19) $g(t) = 2t^2 + t + 4$, find $g(2)$

20) $p(s) = 4s^2 - s + 9$, find $p(9)$

21) $m(u) = 5u + 3$, find $m(2)$

22) $p(s) = 9s^2 + s + 2$, find $p(3)$

✏️ **Evaluate each function.**

1) $h(x) = 3x^2 + 5$, find $h(5)$
 $\Rightarrow h(5) = 80$

2) $h(x) = 3x^2 - x + 3$, find $h(9)$
 $\Rightarrow h(9) = 237$

3) $m(u) = 5u^2 + u + 7$, find $m(6)$
 $\Rightarrow m(6) = 193$

4) $h(x) = 8x^2 + 2$, find $h(1)$
 $\Rightarrow h(1) = 10$

5) $f(x) = 11x^2 - x + 2$, find $f(4)$
 $\Rightarrow f(4) = 174$

6) $f(x) = 11x^2 + 4$, find $f(1)$
 $\Rightarrow f(1) = 15$

7) $g(t) = 2t^2 - t + 2$, find $g(2)$
 $\Rightarrow g(2) = 8$

8) $h(x) = 8x^2 + x + 3$, find $h(8)$
 $\Rightarrow h(8) = 523$

9) $m(u) = 10u^2 + 2$, find $m(6)$
 $\Rightarrow m(6) = 362$

10) $h(x) = 3x^2 + x + 4$, find $h(1)$
 $\Rightarrow h(1) = 8$

11) $g(t) = 7t^2 + 1$, find $g(1)$
 $\Rightarrow g(1) = 8$

12) $m(u) = 10u^2 - u + 8$, find $m(6)$
 $\Rightarrow m(6) = 362$

13) $p(s) = 4s + 2$, find $p(8)$
 $\Rightarrow p(8) = 34$

14) $f(x) = 6x^2 - x + 8$, find $f(7)$
 $\Rightarrow f(7) = 295$

15) $p(s) = 9s + 8$, find $p(3)$
 $\Rightarrow p(3) = 35$

16) $g(t) = 7t^2 - t + 6$, find $g(2)$
 $\Rightarrow g(2) = 32$

17) $g(t) = 7t^2 + t + 7$, find $g(6)$
 $\Rightarrow g(6) = 265$

18) $f(x) = 6x + 7$, find $f(8)$
 $\Rightarrow f(8) = 55$

19) $g(t) = 2t^2 + t + 4$, find $g(2)$
 $\Rightarrow g(2) = 14$

20) $p(s) = 4s^2 - s + 9$, find $p(9)$
 $\Rightarrow p(9) = 324$

21) $m(u) = 5u + 3$, find $m(2)$
 $\Rightarrow m(2) = 13$

22) $p(s) = 9s^2 + s + 2$, find $p(3)$
 $\Rightarrow p(3) = 86$

testinar.com/t/?c=20

✏️ **Perform the indicated operation.**

1) $h(x) = -4x + 6$
   $g(x) = 8x + 1$
   Find $(h - g)(x)$

2) $h(x) = -3x + 5$
   $g(x) = 2x + 4$
   Find $(h + g)(x)$

3) $h(x) = -2x + 6$
   $g(x) = 3x + 4$
   Find $(h - g)(x)$

4) $h(x) = 4x + 8$
   $g(x) = 2x + 3$
   Find $(h + g)(x)$

5) $h(x) = -2x + 8$
   $g(x) = 7x + 4$
   Find $(h - g)(x)$

6) $h(x) = -10x + 6$
   $g(x) = 3x + 4$
   Find $(h - g)(x)$

7) $h(x) = -8x + 6$
   $g(x) = 2x + 2$
   Find $(h - g)(x)$

8) $h(x) = -2x + 5$
   $g(x) = 7x + 1$
   Find $(h + g)(x)$

9) $h(x) = 11x + 7$
   $g(x) = 7x + 4$
   Find $(h + g)(x)$

10) $h(x) = 10x + 5$
    $g(x) = 4x + 4$
    Find $(h + g)(x)$

11) $h(x) = -3x + 7$
    $g(x) = 4x + 1$
    Find $(h - g)(x)$

12) $h(x) = -6x + 5$
    $g(x) = 2x + 4$
    Find $(h + g)(x)$

✏️➤ **Perform the indicated operation.**

1) $h(x) = -4x + 6$
   $g(x) = 8x + 1$
   Find $(h - g)(x)$
   $(h - g)(x) = -12x + 5$

2) $h(x) = -3x + 5$
   $g(x) = 2x + 4$
   Find $(h + g)(x)$
   $(h + g)(x) = -1x + 9$

3) $h(x) = -2x + 6$
   $g(x) = 3x + 4$
   Find $(h - g)(x)$
   $(h - g)(x) = -5x + 2$

4) $h(x) = 4x + 8$
   $g(x) = 2x + 3$
   Find $(h + g)(x)$
   $(h + g)(x) = 6x + 11$

5) $h(x) = -2x + 8$
   $g(x) = 7x + 4$
   Find $(h - g)(x)$
   $(h - g)(x) = -9x + 4$

6) $h(x) = -10x + 6$
   $g(x) = 3x + 4$
   Find $(h - g)(x)$
   $(h - g)(x) = -13x + 2$

7) $h(x) = -8x + 6$
   $g(x) = 2x + 2$
   Find $(h - g)(x)$
   $(h - g)(x) = -10x + 4$

8) $h(x) = -2x + 5$
   $g(x) = 7x + 1$
   Find $(h + g)(x)$
   $(h + g)(x) = 5x + 6$

9) $h(x) = 11x + 7$
   $g(x) = 7x + 4$
   Find $(h + g)(x)$
   $(h + g)(x) = 18x + 11$

10) $h(x) = 10x + 5$
    $g(x) = 4x + 4$
    Find $(h + g)(x)$
    $(h + g)(x) = 14x + 9$

11) $h(x) = -3x + 7$
    $g(x) = 4x + 1$
    Find $(h - g)(x)$
    $(h - g)(x) = -7x + 6$

12) $h(x) = -6x + 5$
    $g(x) = 2x + 4$
    Find $(h + g)(x)$
    $(h + g)(x) = -4x + 9$

✏️ **Perform the indicated operation.**

1) $h(x) = 5x$
   $g(x) = -10x^3 + 10x^2$
   Find $\left(\frac{g}{h}\right)(x)$

2) $h(x) = 10x$
   $g(x) = 6x + 4$
   Find $(h.g)(3)$

3) $h(x) = 11x$
   $g(x) = 7x + 4$
   Find $(h.g)(x)$

4) $h(x) = 6x$
   $g(x) = -12x^3 + 18x^2$
   Find $\left(\frac{g}{h}\right)(x)$

5) $h(x) = 7x$
   $g(x) = -21x^3 + 14x^2$
   Find $\left(\frac{g}{h}\right)(2)$

6) $h(x) = -7x$
   $g(x) = 8x - 2$
   Find $(h.g)(x)$

7) $h(x) = 2x$
   $g(x) = 4x + 4$
   Find $(h.g)(1)$

8) $h(x) = 9x$
   $g(x) = -27x^3 + 36x^2$
   Find $\left(\frac{g}{h}\right)(x)$

9) $h(x) = 2x$
   $g(x) = 8x^3 + 6x^2$
   Find $\left(\frac{g}{h}\right)(x)$

10) $h(x) = 3x$
    $g(x) = 6x + 4$
    Find $(h.g)(3)$

11) $h(x) = -5x$
    $g(x) = 6x - 2$
    Find $(h.g)(x)$

12) $h(x) = 2x$
    $g(x) = 6x + 3$
    Find $(h.g)(x)$

✏️ **Perform the indicated operation.**

1) $h(x) = 5x$
   $g(x) = -10x^3 + 10x^2$
   Find $\left(\frac{g}{h}\right)(x)$
   $\left(\frac{g}{h}\right)(x) = -2x^2 + 2x$

2) $h(x) = 10x$
   $g(x) = 6x + 4$
   Find $(h.g)(3)$
   $(h.g)(x) = 660$

3) $h(x) = 11x$
   $g(x) = 7x + 4$
   Find $(h.g)(x)$
   $(h.g)(x) = 77x^2 + 44x$

4) $h(x) = 6x$
   $g(x) = -12x^3 + 18x^2$
   Find $\left(\frac{g}{h}\right)(x)$
   $\left(\frac{g}{h}\right)(x) = -2x^2 + 3x$

5) $h(x) = 7x$
   $g(x) = -21x^3 + 14x^2$
   Find $\left(\frac{g}{h}\right)(2)$
   $\left(\frac{g}{h}\right)(x) = -8$

6) $h(x) = -7x$
   $g(x) = 8x - 2$
   Find $(h.g)(x)$
   $(h.g)(x) = -56x^2 + 14x$

7) $h(x) = 2x$
   $g(x) = 4x + 4$
   Find $(h.g)(1)$
   $(h.g)(x) = 16$

8) $h(x) = 9x$
   $g(x) = -27x^3 + 36x^2$
   Find $\left(\frac{g}{h}\right)(x)$
   $\left(\frac{g}{h}\right)(x) = -3x^2 + 4x$

9) $h(x) = 2x$
   $g(x) = 8x^3 + 6x^2$
   Find $\left(\frac{g}{h}\right)(x)$
   $\left(\frac{g}{h}\right)(x) = 4x^2 + 3x$

10) $h(x) = 3x$
    $g(x) = 6x + 4$
    Find $(h.g)(3)$
    $(h.g)(x) = 198$

11) $h(x) = -5x$
    $g(x) = 6x - 2$
    Find $(h.g)(x)$
    $(h.g)(x) = -30x^2 + 10x$

12) $h(x) = 2x$
    $g(x) = 6x + 3$
    Find $(h.g)(x)$
    $(h.g)(x) = 12x^2 + 6x$

✏️ **Perform the indicated operation.**

1) $f(x) = 8x + 8$
   $g(x) = 4x + 3$
   Find $f(f(x)))$

2) $f(x) = 7x + 2$
   $g(x) = 2x + 3$
   Find $g(g(4)))$

3) $f(x) = 9x + 3$
   $g(x) = 5x + 1$
   Find $g(g(3)))$

4) $f(x) = 11x + 1$
   $g(x) = 6x + 1$
   Find $g(g(1)))$

5) $f(x) = 5x + 4$
   $g(x) = 7x + 2$
   Find $f(g(x)))$

6) $f(x) = 11x + 2$
   $g(x) = 2x + 1$
   Find $f(f(x)))$

7) $f(x) = 8x + 3$
   $g(x) = 2x + 2$
   Find $f(g(x)))$

8) $f(x) = 7x + 6$
   $g(x) = -2x + 3$
   Find $f(g(x)))$

9) $f(x) = 10x + 7$
   $g(x) = 6x + 4$
   Find $g(g(3)))$

10) $f(x) = 8x + 8$
    $g(x) = 3x + 2$
    Find $f(g(-3)))$

11) $f(x) = 11x + 7$
    $g(x) = 6x + 4$
    Find $f(g(-4)))$

12) $f(x) = 6x + 3$
    $g(x) = 5x + 3$
    Find $f(g(-1)))$

➤ **Perform the indicated operation.**

1) $f(x) = 8x + 8$
   $g(x) = 4x + 3$
   Find $f(f(x)))$
   $f(g(x)) = 64x + 72$

2) $f(x) = 7x + 2$
   $g(x) = 2x + 3$
   Find $g(g(4)))$
   $g(g(4)) = 25$

3) $f(x) = 9x + 3$
   $g(x) = 5x + 1$
   Find $g(g(3)))$
   $g(g(3)) = 81$

4) $f(x) = 11x + 1$
   $g(x) = 6x + 1$
   Find $g(g(1)))$
   $g(g(1)) = 43$

5) $f(x) = 5x + 4$
   $g(x) = 7x + 2$
   Find $f(g(x)))$
   $f(g(x)) = 35x + 14$

6) $f(x) = 11x + 2$
   $g(x) = 2x + 1$
   Find $f(f(x)))$
   $f(g(x)) = 121x + 24$

7) $f(x) = 8x + 3$
   $g(x) = 2x + 2$
   Find $f(g(x)))$
   $f(g(x)) = 16x + 19$

8) $f(x) = 7x + 6$
   $g(x) = -2x + 3$
   Find $f(g(x)))$
   $f(g(x)) = -14x + 27$

9) $f(x) = 10x + 7$
   $g(x) = 6x + 4$
   Find $g(g(3)))$
   $g(g(3)) = 136$

10) $f(x) = 8x + 8$
    $g(x) = 3x + 2$
    Find $f(g(-3)))$
    $f(g(-3)) = -48$

11) $f(x) = 11x + 7$
    $g(x) = 6x + 4$
    Find $f(g(-4)))$
    $f(g(-4)) = -213$

12) $f(x) = 6x + 3$
    $g(x) = 5x + 3$
    Find $f(g(-1)))$
    $f(g(-1)) = -9$

TASC Test Review

The Test Assessing Secondary Completion, commonly known as the TASC or high school equivalency degree, is a standardized test. The TASC is a standardized test to verify that examinees have knowledge in core content areas equivalent to that of graduating high school seniors.

There are five subject area tests on TASC:

- Reading;
- Writing;
- Social Studies;
- Science;
- Mathematics.

The TASC Mathematics test is a 105-minute test that covers basic mathematics topics, quantitative problem-solving and algebraic questions. There are two Mathematics sections on the TASC. The first section contains 40 multiple choice questions where calculators are permitted. You have 55 minutes to complete this section. The second section contains 12 Gridded-Response questions. Calculator is NOT allowed in the second part. Test takers have 50 minutes to answer all questions in this section. Examinees will also be given a page of mathematic formulas to use during the test.

In this book, there are two complete TASC Mathematics Tests. Take these tests to see what score you'll be able to receive on a real TASC test.

Good luck!

Time to refine your quantitative reasoning skill with a practice test

In this section, there are two complete TASCT Mathematics practice tests. Take these tests to simulate the test day experience. After you've finished, score your tests using the answer keys.

Before You Start

- You'll need a pencil, a calculator, and a timer to take the test.
- It's okay to guess. You won't lose any points if you're wrong. So be sure to answer every question.
- After you've finished the test, review the answer key to see where you went wrong.
- **Calculators are only permitted for the first section of the TASC Test.**
- The TASC Mathematics test contains a formula sheet, which displays formulas relating to geometric measurement and certain algebra concepts. Formulas are provided to test-takers so that they may focus on application, rather than the memorization, of formulas.
- For each multiple-choice question, there are four possible answers. Choose which one is best. For grids in questions, write your answer in the answer boxes at the top of the grid. Then, as shown below fill in a bubble under each box in which you wrote your answer.

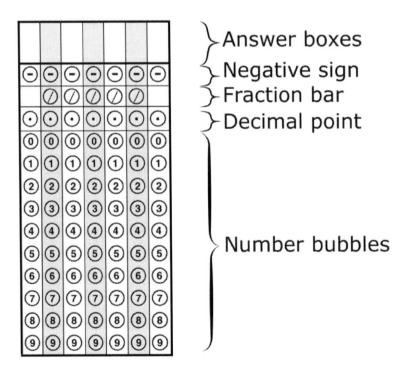

Good Luck!

TASC Mathematics
Practice Test 1

2019

Two Parts

Total number of questions: 52

Part 1 (Calculator): 40 questions

Part 2 (Calculator): 12 questions

Total time for two parts: 105 Minutes

TASC Practice Tests Answer Sheet

Remove (or photocopy) these answer sheets and use them to complete the practice tests.

TASC Practice Test 1 – Section 1 Answer Sheet

1) (A) (B) (C) (D)   2) (A) (B) (C) (D)   3) (A) (B) (C) (D)

4) (A) (B) (C) (D)   5) (A) (B) (C) (D)   6) (A) (B) (C) (D)

7) (A) (B) (C) (D)   8) (A) (B) (C) (D)   9) (A) (B) (C) (D)

10) (A) (B) (C) (D)   11) (A) (B) (C) (D)   12) (A) (B) (C) (D)

13) (A) (B) (C) (D)   14) (A) (B) (C) (D)   15) (A) (B) (C) (D)

16) (A) (B) (C) (D)   17) (A) (B) (C) (D)   18) (A) (B) (C) (D)

19) (A) (B) (C) (D)   20) (A) (B) (C) (D)   21) (A) (B) (C) (D)

22) (A) (B) (C) (D)   23) (A) (B) (C) (D)   24) (A) (B) (C) (D)

25) (A) (B) (C) (D)   26) (A) (B) (C) (D)   27) (A) (B) (C) (D)

28) (A) (B) (C) (D)   29) (A) (B) (C) (D)   30) (A) (B) (C) (D)

31) (A) (B) (C) (D)   32) (A) (B) (C) (D)   33) (A) (B) (C) (D)

34) (A) (B) (C) (D)   35) (A) (B) (C) (D)   36) (A) (B) (C) (D)

37) (A) (B) (C) (D)   38) (A) (B) (C) (D)   39) (A) (B) (C) (D)

40) (A) (B) (C) (D)

TASC Practice Test 1: Section 2: Grid-ins Questions

41)

42)

43)

44)

45)

46)

47)

48)

49)

50)

51)

52)

TASC Test Mathematics Formula Sheet

Cylinder: $V = \pi r^2 h$

Pyramid: $V = \frac{1}{3}Bh$

Cone: $V = \frac{1}{3}\pi r^2 h$

Sphere: $V = \frac{4}{3}\pi r^3$

coordinate Geometry Midpoint of the segment AB:

$m\left(\frac{x_2 + x_1}{2}, \frac{y_1 + y_2}{2}\right)$

Distance from A to B:

$d = \sqrt{(x_1 - x_2)^2 + (y_1 - y_2)^2}$

Slope of a line:

$m = \frac{(Y_2 - Y_1)}{(X_2 - X_1)}$

Special Factoring:

$a^2 - b^2 = (a + b)(a - b)$

$a^2 + 2ab + b^2 = (a + b)(a + b) = (a + b)^2$

$a^2 - 2ab + b^2 = (a - b)(a - b) = (a - b)^2$

$a^3 + b^3 = (a + b)(a^2 - ab + b^2)$

$a^3 - b^3 = (a - b)(a^2 + ab + b^2)$

Quadratic Formula

for $ax^2 + bx + c = 0$

$x = \frac{-b \pm \sqrt{b^2 - 4ac}}{2a}$

Interest

Simple Interest:

$I = prt$

Interest Formula (compounded n times per year):

$A = p\left(1 + \frac{r}{n}\right)^{nt}$

A = Amount after t years

p = principal

r = annual interest rate

t = time in years

I = Interest

Trigonometric Identities

Pythagorean Theorem: $a^2 + b^2 = c^2$

$sin\theta = \frac{opp}{hyp}$

$cos\theta = \frac{adj}{hyp}$

$tan\theta = \frac{opp}{adj}$

$sin^2\theta + cos^2\theta = 1$

Density $= \frac{Mass}{Volume}$

Central Angle

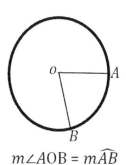

$m\angle AOB = m\widehat{AB}$

Inscribed Angle

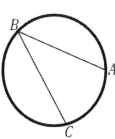

$m\angle ABC = \frac{1}{2}m\,\widehat{AC}$

Intersecting Chords Theorem

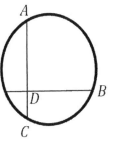

$A \cdot B = C \cdot D$

Probability

Permutations: $_nP_r = \frac{n!}{(n-r)!}$

Combinations: $_nC_r = \frac{n!}{(n-r)!r!}$

Multiplication rule (independent events): P(A and B) = P(A)·P(B)

Multiplication rule (general): P(A and B) = P(A)·P(B|A)

Addition rule: P(A or B) = P(A) + P(B) − P(A and B)

Conditional Probability: $P(B|A) = \frac{P(AandB)}{P(A)}$

Arithmetic Sequence: $a_n = a_1 + (n_1)d$ where a_n is the nth term, is the first term, a_1 and d is the common difference.

Geometric Sequence: $a_n = a_1 r^{(n-1)}$ where a_n is the nth term, a_1 is the first term, and r is the common ratio.

1) If 50% of A is 25 of B, then B is what percent of A?

   (A) 200%

   (B) 250%

   (C) 150%

   (D) 180%

2) Find the average of the following numbers: $17, 13, 7, 21, 22$

   (A) 17

   (B) 16

   (C) 22

   (D) 25

3) John traveled 180 km in 3 hours and Alice traveled 270 km in 9 hours. What is the ratio of the average speed of John to average speed of Alice?

   (A) $2 : 1$

   (B) $2 : 3$

   (C) $1 : 3$

   (D) $1 : 5$

4) The width of a box is one third of its length. The height of the box is one third of its width. If the length of the box is 36 cm, what is the volume of the box?

   (A) $1,728$ cm^3

   (B) $1,490$ cm^3

   (C) $1,569$ cm^3

   (D) $1,289$ cm^3

5) When a number is subtracted from 25 and the difference is divided by that number, the result is 4. What is the value of the number?

   (A) 4

   (B) 10

   (C) 8

   (D) 5

6) What is the value of 7^4?

   (A) $2,809$

   (B) $1,979$

   (C) $2,379$

   (D) $2,401$

---

7) 27 is What percent of 30?

   (A) 90%

   (B) 99%

   (C) 85%

   (D) 78%

---

8) Right triangle ABC has two legs of lengths 5 cm (AB) and 12 cm (AC). What is the length of the third side (BC)?

   (A) 18 cm

   (B) 12 cm

   (C) 21 cm

   (D) 13 cm

---

9) An angle is equal to one eighth of its supplement. What is the measure of that angle?

   (A) $20°$

   (B) $22°$

   (C) $32°$

   (D) $18°$

---

10) In five successive hours, a car travels 35 km, 40 km, 45 km, 25 km and 50 km. In the next five hours, it travels with an average speed of 45 km per hour. Find the total distance the car traveled in 10 hours.

   (A) 401

   (B) 391

   (C) 430

   (D) 420

11) A taxi driver earns $12 per 1—hour work. If he works 8 hours a day and in 1 hour he uses 2—liters petrol with price $1 for 1—liter. How much money does he earn in one day?

    (A) $75
    (B) $80
    (C) $86
    (D) $92

12) How long does a 380—miles trip take moving at 40 miles per hour (mph)?

    (A) 8 hours and 30 minutes
    (B) 8 hours and 25 minutes
    (C) 10 hours and 25 minutes
    (D) 9 hours and 30 minutes

13) A $50 shirt now selling for $25 is discounted by what percent?

    (A) 50%
    (B) 29%
    (C) 64%
    (D) 25%

14) The ratio of boys and girls in a class is 3 : 8. If there are 55 students in the class, how many more boys should be enrolled to make the ratio 1 : 1?

    (A) 15
    (B) 12
    (C) 18
    (D) 10

15) A rope weighs 700 grams per meter of length. What is the weight in kilograms of 13.2 meters of this rope? (1 kilograms = 1000 grams)

    (A) 9.350 kg
    (B) 9.240 kg
    (C) 10.210 kg
    (D) 10.250 kg

16) The average weight of 15 girls in a class is 60 kg and the average weight of 30 boys in the same class is 66 kg. What is the average weight of all the 75 students in that class?

(A) 69 kg

(B) 72 kg

(C) 64 kg

(D) 59 kg

17) Which of the following could be the product of two consecutive prime numbers?

(A) 2

(B) 10

(C) 14

(D) 15

18) The price of a car was $\$20,000$ in 2016, $\$18,000$ in 2018 and $\$16,200$ in 2019. What is the rate of depreciation of the price of car per year?

(A) 10%

(B) 20%

(C) 25%

(D) 15%

19) Sophia purchased a sofa for $\$560.50$. The sofa is regularly priced at $\$1,121$. What was the percent discount Sophia received on the sofa?

(A) 50%

(B) 40%

(C) 60%

(D) 65%

20) The price of a sofa is decreased by 15% to $\$748$. What was its original price?

(A) $\$820$

(B) $\$950$

(C) $\$790$

(D) $\$880$

21) The score of Emma was one third that of Ava and the score of Mia was twice that of Ava. If the score of Mia was 90, what is the score of Emma?

(A) 12

(B) 18

(C) 15

(D) 25

22) The average of five consecutive numbers is 32. What is the smallest number?

(A) 36

(B) 30

(C) 25

(D) 15

23) The price of a laptop is decreased by 10% to $\$378$. What is its original price?

(A) $\$449$

(B) $\$378$

(C) $\$420$

(D) $\$398$

24) What is the median of these numbers? $4, 9, 13, 8, 15, 18, 5$

(A) 9

(B) 18

(C) 15

(D) 13

25) If 35% of a class are girls, and 20% of girls play tennis, what percent of the class play tennis?

(A) 7%

(B) 13%

(C) 9%

(D) 19%

26) One third of 12 is equal to $\frac{2}{3}$ of what number?

    (A) 9

    (B) 12

    (C) 6

    (D) 7

---

27) How many tiles of 10 cm^2 is needed to cover a floor of dimension 8 cm by 35 cm?

    (A) 28

    (B) 24

    (C) 32

    (D) 36

---

28) Which of the following values for x and y satisfy the following system of equations?

$$\begin{cases} x + 2y = 12 \\ 3x + 5y = 18 \end{cases}$$

    (A) $x = 24,\ y = 15$

    (B) $x = 24,\ y = -18$

    (C) $x = -24,\ y = 18$

    (D) $x = -18,\ y = 24$

---

29) A chemical solution contains 5% alcohol. If there is 30 ml of alcohol, what is the volume of the solution?

    (A) 450 ml

    (B) 550 ml

    (C) 700 ml

    (D) 600 ml

---

30) The surface area of a cylinder is $150\,\pi$ cm^2. If its height is 10 cm, what is the radius of the cylinder?

    (A) 15 cm

    (B) -15 cm

    (C) 5 cm

    (D) 10 cm

31) In 2000, the average worker's income increased $\$4,000$ per year starting from $\$21,000$ annual salary. Which equation represents income greater than average? ($I =$ income, $x =$ number of years after 2000)

(A) $I \leq 4000\,x - 21000$

(B) $I \geq -4000\,x + 21000$

(C) $I > 4000 + 21000\,x$

(D) $I > 4000\,x + 21000$

32) A bank is offering 4% simple interest on a savings account. If you deposit $\$7,000$, how much interest will you earn in three years?

(A) 868

(B) 820

(C) 834

(D) 840

33) A boat sails 40 miles south and then 30 miles east. How far is the boat from its start point?

(A) 50 miles

(B) 36 miles

(C) 49 miles

(D) 60 miles

34) A bag contains 18 balls: two green, five black, eight blue, a brown, a red and one white. If 17 balls are removed from the bag at random, what is the probability that a brown ball has been removed?

(A) $\frac{17}{18}$

(B) $\frac{18}{17}$

(C) $\frac{1}{17}$

(D) $\frac{1}{18}$

35) The area of a circle is less than $49\,\pi$. Which of the following can be the circumference of the circle? (Select one or more answer choices)

(A) $12\,\pi$

(B) $15\,\pi$

(C) $18\,\pi$

(D) $20\,\pi$

36) Which of the following lists shows the fractions in order from least to greatest? $\frac{3}{4}, \frac{2}{7}, \frac{3}{8}, \frac{5}{11}$

(A) $\frac{2}{7}, \frac{3}{8}, \frac{5}{11}, \frac{3}{4}$

(B) $\frac{3}{4}, \frac{2}{7}, \frac{5}{11}, \frac{3}{8}$

(C) $\frac{3}{8}, \frac{2}{7}, \frac{3}{4}, \frac{5}{11}$

(D) $\frac{5}{11}, \frac{3}{4}, \frac{2}{7}, \frac{3}{8}$

37) The marked price of a computer is D dollar. Its price decreased by (20\%\) in January and later increased by 10% in February. What is the final price of the computer in D dollar?

(A) 0.80 D

(B) 0.88 D

(C) 80 D

(D) 88 D

38) How many possible outfit combinations come from seven shirts, two slacks, and five ties?

(A) 64

(B) 75

(C) 85

(D) 70

39) In the $x\,y$—plane, the point $(5, 3)$ and $(6, 4)$ are on line A. Which of the following points could also be on line A? (Select one or more answer choices)

(A) $(-1, 2)$

(B) $(5, 7)$

(C) $(3, 4)$

(D) $(-1, -2)$

40) If the area of trapezoid is 126 cm, what is the perimeter of the trapezoid?

(A) 65 cm

(B) 38 cm

(C) 46 cm

(D) 40 cm

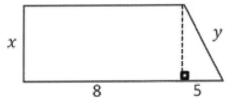

TASC Mathematics
Practice Test 1

Section 2
(No Calculator)

12 questions
Total time for this section: 55 Minutes

You may **NOT** use a calculator on this Section.

41) If $2x - 6 = 10.5$, What is the value of $3x + 2$?

Write your answer in the box below.

---

42) $-16 + 6 \times (-5) - [6 + 22 \times (-4)] \div 2 + 5 = ?$

Write your answer in the box below.

---

43) What is the value of $f(3)$ for the following function f?
   $f(x) = x^2 + 4x$

Write your answer in the box below.

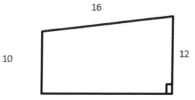

---

44) The perimeter of the trapezoid below is 58. What is its area?

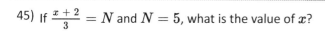

Write your answer in the box below.

---

45) If $\frac{x+2}{3} = N$ and $N = 5$, what is the value of x?

Write your answer in the box below.

---

46) The volume of cube A is $\frac{1}{4}$ of its surface area. What is the length of an edge of cube A?

Write your answer in the box below.

47) What is the area of an isosceles right triangle that has one leg that measures 4?

Write your answer in the box below.

48) The average of $13, 16, 24$ and x is 15. What is the value of x?

Write your answer in the box below.

49) A ladder leans against a wall forming a $60°$ angle between the ground and the ladder. If the bottom of the ladder is 45 feet away from the wall, how many feet is the ladder?

Write your answer in the box below.

50) From last year, the price of gasoline has increased from $\$1.30$ per gallon to $\$1.75$ per gallon. The new price is what percent of the original price?

Write your answer in the box below.

51) If the ratio of $3\ a$ to $4\ b$ is $\frac{1}{10}$, what is the ratio of a to b?

Write your answer in the box below.

52) A construction company is building a wall. The company can build 50 cm of the wall per minute. After 45 minutes $\frac{2}{3}$ of the wall is completed. How many meters is the wall?

Write your answer in the box below.

TASC Mathematics
Practice Test 2

2020

Two Parts

Total number of questions: 52

Part 1 (Calculator): 40 questions

Part 2 (Calculator): 12 questions

Total time for two parts: 105 Minutes

TASC Practice Tests Answer Sheet

Remove (or photocopy) these answer sheets and use them to complete the practice tests.

TASC Practice Test 2 – Section 1 Answer Sheet

1) Ⓐ Ⓑ Ⓒ Ⓓ   2) Ⓐ Ⓑ Ⓒ Ⓓ   3) Ⓐ Ⓑ Ⓒ Ⓓ

4) Ⓐ Ⓑ Ⓒ Ⓓ   5) Ⓐ Ⓑ Ⓒ Ⓓ   6) Ⓐ Ⓑ Ⓒ Ⓓ

7) Ⓐ Ⓑ Ⓒ Ⓓ   8) Ⓐ Ⓑ Ⓒ Ⓓ   9) Ⓐ Ⓑ Ⓒ Ⓓ

10) Ⓐ Ⓑ Ⓒ Ⓓ   11) Ⓐ Ⓑ Ⓒ Ⓓ   12) Ⓐ Ⓑ Ⓒ Ⓓ

13) Ⓐ Ⓑ Ⓒ Ⓓ   14) Ⓐ Ⓑ Ⓒ Ⓓ   15) Ⓐ Ⓑ Ⓒ Ⓓ

16) Ⓐ Ⓑ Ⓒ Ⓓ   17) Ⓐ Ⓑ Ⓒ Ⓓ   18) Ⓐ Ⓑ Ⓒ Ⓓ

19) Ⓐ Ⓑ Ⓒ Ⓓ   20) Ⓐ Ⓑ Ⓒ Ⓓ   21) Ⓐ Ⓑ Ⓒ Ⓓ

22) Ⓐ Ⓑ Ⓒ Ⓓ   23) Ⓐ Ⓑ Ⓒ Ⓓ   24) Ⓐ Ⓑ Ⓒ Ⓓ

25) Ⓐ Ⓑ Ⓒ Ⓓ   26) Ⓐ Ⓑ Ⓒ Ⓓ   27) Ⓐ Ⓑ Ⓒ Ⓓ

28) Ⓐ Ⓑ Ⓒ Ⓓ   29) Ⓐ Ⓑ Ⓒ Ⓓ   30) Ⓐ Ⓑ Ⓒ Ⓓ

31) Ⓐ Ⓑ Ⓒ Ⓓ   32) Ⓐ Ⓑ Ⓒ Ⓓ   33) Ⓐ Ⓑ Ⓒ Ⓓ

34) Ⓐ Ⓑ Ⓒ Ⓓ   35) Ⓐ Ⓑ Ⓒ Ⓓ   36) Ⓐ Ⓑ Ⓒ Ⓓ

37) Ⓐ Ⓑ Ⓒ Ⓓ   38) Ⓐ Ⓑ Ⓒ Ⓓ   39) Ⓐ Ⓑ Ⓒ Ⓓ

40) Ⓐ Ⓑ Ⓒ Ⓓ

TASC Practice Test 2: Section 2: Grid-ins Questions

41)

42)

43)

44)

45)

46)

47)

48)

49)

50)

51)

52)

TASC Test Mathematics Formula Sheet

Cylinder: $V = \pi r^2 h$

Pyramid: $V = \frac{1}{3}Bh$

Cone: $V = \frac{1}{3}\pi r^2 h$

Sphere: $V = \frac{4}{3}\pi r^3$

coordinate Geometry Midpoint of the segment AB:

$m\left(\frac{x_2+x_1}{2}, \frac{y_1+y_2}{2}\right)$

Distance from A to B:

$d = \sqrt{(x_1 - x_2)^2 + (y_1 - y_2)^2}$

Slope of a line:

$m = \frac{(Y_2 - Y_1)}{(X_2 - X_1)}$

Special Factoring:

$a^2 - b^2 = (a+b)(a-b)$

$a^2 + 2ab + b^2 = (a+b)(a+b) = (a+b)^2$

$a^2 - 2ab + b^2 = (a-b)(a-b) = (a-b)^2$

$a^3 + b^3 = (a+b)(a^2 - ab + b^2)$

$a^3 - b^3 = (a-b)(a^2 + ab + b^2)$

Quadratic Formula

for $ax^2 + bx + c = 0$

$x = \frac{-b \pm \sqrt{b^2 - 4ac}}{2a}$

Interest

Simple Interest:

$I = prt$

Interest Formula (compounded n times per year):

$A = p(1 + \frac{r}{n})^{nt}$

A = Amount after t years

p = principal

r = annual interest rate

t = time in years

I = Interest

Trigonometric Identities

Pythagorean Theorem: $a^2 + b^2 = c^2$

$sin\theta = \frac{opp}{hyp}$

$cos\theta = \frac{adj}{hyp}$

$tan\theta = \frac{opp}{adj}$

$sin^2\theta + cos^2\theta = 1$

Density $= \frac{Mass}{Volume}$

Central Angle	Inscribed Angle	Intersecting Chords Theorem
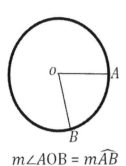	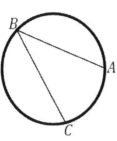	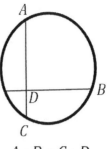
$m\angle AOB = m\widehat{AB}$	$m\angle ABC = \frac{1}{2}m\,\widehat{AC}$	$A \cdot B = C \cdot D$

Probability

Permutations: $_nP_r = \dfrac{n!}{(n-r)!}$

Combinations: $_nC_r = \dfrac{n!}{(n-r)!\,r!}$

Multiplication rule (independent events): P(A and B) = P(A)·P(B)

Multiplication rule (general): P(A and B) = P(A)·P(B|A)

Addition rule: P(A or B) = P(A) + P(B) − P(A and B)

Conditional Probability: $P(B|A) = \dfrac{P(A and B)}{P(A)}$

Arithmetic Sequence: $a_n = a_1 + (n_1)d$ where a_n is the nth term, is the first term, a_1 and d is the common difference.

Geometric Sequence: $a_n = a_1 r^{(n-1)}$ where a_n is the nth term, a_1 is the first term, and r is the common ratio.

1) What is the volume of a box with the following dimensions?
   Height $= 3$ cm Width $= 5$ cm Length $= 8$ cm

   (A) 120 cm^3

   (B) 130 cm^3

   (C) 142 cm^3

   (D) 112 cm^3

2) Which of the following points lies on the line $x + 3y = 8$?

   (A) $(-2, 3)$

   (B) $(2, 2)$

   (C) $(-2, 3)$

   (D) $(-3, 4)$

3) Last week $20,000$ fans attended a football match. This week three times as many bought tickets, but one fifth of them cancelled their tickets. How many are attending this week?

   (A) $45,000$

   (B) $38,000$

   (C) $48,000$

   (D) $42,000$

4) Two dice are thrown simultaneously, what is the probability of getting a sum of 6 or 9?

   (A) $\frac{1}{2}$

   (B) $\frac{2}{5}$

   (C) $\frac{1}{4}$

   (D) $\frac{1}{3}$

5)
   What is the value of 4^5?

   (A) $1,024$

   (B) $1,125$

   (C) $1,140$

   (D) $1,030$

6) What is the area of a square whose diagonal is 10?

(A) 150

(B) 50

(C) 80

(D) 120

7) What is the median of these numbers? $7, 25, 29, 19, 63, 44, 35$

(A) 29

(B) 43

(C) 75

(D) 120

8) Right triangle ABC has two legs of lengths 5 cm (AB) and 12 cm (AC). What is the length of the third side (BC)?

(A) 12

(B) 24

(C) 42

(D) 13

9) What is the equivalent temperature of $104°$ F in Celsius?
$C = \frac{3}{5} (F - 29)$

(A) 45

(B) 32

(C) 44

(D) 72

10)
Simplify the expression.
$(4 x^3 + 3 x^2 - 4 x^4) - (2 x^2 + 3 x^4 - 5 x^3)$

(A) $9 x^3 + x^2 - 7 x^4$

(B) $5 x^3 - x^2 - 3 x^4$

(C) $2 x^3 + 3 x^2 - 3 x^4$

(D) $9 x^3 + 3 x^2 + 5 x^4$

11) If 36% of a number is 9, what is the number?

(A) 13

(B) 61

(C) 18

(D) 25

12) Which of the following shows the numbers in descending order?
$\frac{1}{3}, 0.82, 55\%, \frac{4}{9}$

(A) $55\%, \frac{4}{9}, \frac{1}{1}, 0.82$

(B) $0.82, 55\%, \frac{4}{9}, \frac{1}{1}$

(C) $\frac{1}{3}, \frac{4}{9}, 55\%, 0.82$

(D) $\frac{4}{9}, \frac{1}{3}, 55\%, 0.82$

13) The circle graph below shows all Mr. Green's expenses for last month. If he spent $\$616$ on his car, how much did he spend for his rent?

(A) $\$780$

(B) $\$420$

(C) $\$756$

(D) $\$921$

14) Jason is 9 miles ahead of Joe running at 5.5 miles per hour and Joe is running at the speed of 7 miles per hour. How long does it take Joe to catch Jason?

(A) 6 hours

(B) 10 hours

(C) 4 hours

(D) 9 hours

15) 60 students took an exam and 12 of them failed. What percent of the students passed the exam?

(A) 90%

(B) 110%

(C) 80%

(D) 40%

16) A bank is offering 4.5% simple interest on a savings account. If you deposit $\$15,000$, how much interest will you earn in two years?

(A) $\$1,270$

(B) $\$1,350$

(C) $\$1,420$

(D) $\$1,824$

17) Simplify $3\,x^2\,y^3\,(4\,x^2\,y)^3 =$

(A) $192\,x^8\,y^6$

(B) $150\,x^4\,y^6$

(C) $180\,x^5\,y^3$

(D) $12\,x^4\,y^9$

18) A football team had $\$21,000$ to spend on supplies. The team spent $\$12,000$ on new balls. New sport shoes cost $\$150$ each. Which of the following inequalities represent the number of new shoes the team can purchase?

(A) $150\,x\,+\,12,000\,\leq\,21,000$

(B) $150\,x\,+\,12,000\,\geq\,21,000$

(C) $21,000\,x\,+\,12,000\,\geq\,150$

(D) $21,000\,x\,+\,150\,\geq\,12,000$

19) A card is drawn at random from a standard 54–card deck, what is the probability that the card is of Hearts? (The deck includes 12 of each suit clubs, diamonds, hearts, and spades)

(A) $\frac{1}{4}$

(B) $\frac{1}{6}$

(C) $\frac{1}{3}$

(D) $\frac{2}{3}$

20) In two successive years, the population of a town is increased by 15% and 20%. What percent of the population is increased after two years?

(A) 38%

(B) 22%

(C) 89%

(D) 44%

21) The average of five numbers is 26.4. If a sixth number that is greater than 42 is added, then, which of the following could be the new average? (Select one or more answer choices)

(A) 25

(B) 28

(C) 27

(D) 30

22) What is the surface area of the cylinder below?

(A) $44\,\pi$

(B) $32\,\pi$

(C) $54\,\pi$

(D) $66\,\pi$

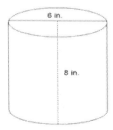

23) The square of a number is $\frac{36}{64}$. What is the cube of that number?

(A) $\frac{216}{512}$

(B) $\frac{214}{525}$

(C) $\frac{115}{465}$

(D) $\frac{120}{546}$

24) Anita's trick–or–treat bag contains 12 pieces of chocolate, 18 suckers, 18 pieces of gum, 24 pieces of licorice. If she randomly pulls a piece of candy from her bag, what is the probability of her pulling out a piece of sucker?

(A) $\frac{1}{5}$

(B) $\frac{1}{4}$

(C) $\frac{2}{3}$

(D) $\frac{1}{8}$

25) The perimeter of the trapezoid below is 45 cm. What is its area?

(A) $135\,\text{cm}^2$

(B) $229\,\text{cm}^2$

(C) $156\,\text{cm}^2$

(D) $190\,\text{cm}^2$

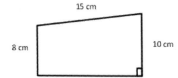

26) If 130% of a number is 65, then what is the 84% of that number?

(A) 56

(B) 32

(C) 42

(D) 93

27) What is the value of x in the following equation?
$$\frac{2}{5}x + \frac{1}{4} = \frac{1}{2}$$

(A) $\frac{5}{8}$

(B) $\frac{2}{7}$

(C) $\frac{7}{9}$

(D) $\frac{3}{8}$

28) Jason needs an 75% average in his writing class to pass. On his first 4 exams, he earned scores of $64\%, 55\%, 82\%$, and 80%. What is the minimum score Jason can earn on his fifth and final test to pass?

(A) 39

(B) 78

(C) 66

(D) 94

29) Mr. Brown saves $\$2,800$ out of his monthly family income of $\$56,000$. What fractional part of his income does he save?

(A) $\frac{1}{20}$

(B) $\frac{4}{23}$

(C) $\frac{2}{19}$

(D) $\frac{1}{19}$

30) Which of the following graphs represents the compound inequality $-2 \leq 2x - 4 < 8$?

(A)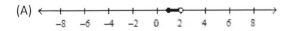

(C)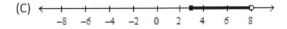

(B)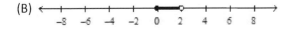

(D)

31) The length of a rectangle is 4 meters greater than 3 times its width. The perimeter of the rectangle is 56 meters. What is the area of the rectangle in meters?

(A) 132

(B) 162

(C) 189

(D) 121

32) The ratio of boys and girls in a class is $3 : 9$. If there are 48 students in the class, how many more boys should be enrolled to make the ratio $1 : 1$?

(A) 21

(B) 32

(C) 24

(D) 34

33) What is the perimeter of a square in centimeters that has an area of 561.69 cm^2?

(A) 94.8

(B) 92

(C) 82

(D) 82.94

34) What is the value of x in the following system of equations?
$$2x + 4y = 18$$
$$4x - y = -9$$

(A) $x = -1, y = 5$

(B) $x = -2, y = 4$

(C) $x = 1, y = -5$

(D) $x = -1, y = -5$

35) In a stadium the ratio of home fans to visiting fans in a crowd is $4 : 9$. Which of the following could be the total number of fans in the stadium?

(A) $12,324$

(B) $42,326$

(C) $44,566$

(D) $66,812$

36) The average of 6 numbers is 24. The average of 4 of those numbers is 12. What is the average of the other two numbers?

(A) 48

(B) 22

(C) 34

37) A swimming pool holds 2,500 cubic feet of water. The swimming pool is 25 feet long and 20 feet wide. How deep is the swimming pool?

(A) 15

(B) 5

(C) 10

(D) 25

(E) 25

38) The mean of 40 test scores was calculated as 80. But, it turned out that one of the scores was misread as 92 but it was 64. What is the correct mean of the test scores?

(A) 79.3

(B) 49.7

(C) 68.2

(D) 88.8

39) The perimeter of a rectangular yard is 120 meters. What is its length if its width is twice its length?

(A) 18 meters

(B) 24 meters

(C) 60 meters

(D) 20 meters

40) Mr. Carlos family are choosing a menu for their reception. They have 3 choices of appetizers, 4 choices of entrees, 6 choices of cake. How many different menu combinations are possible for them to choose?

(A) 60

(B) 72

(C) 68

(D) 78

TASC Mathematics
Practice Test 2

Section 2
(No Calculator)

12 questions
Total time for this section: 55 Minutes

You may **NOT** use a calculator on this Section.

41) A tree 38.4 feet tall casts a shadow 12 feet long. Jack is 8 feet tall. How long is Jack's shadow?

Write your answer in the box below.

42) What is the slope of a line that is perpendicular to the line $3x + 2y = 8$?

Write your answer in the box below.

43) The area of a rectangular yard is 84 square meters. What is its width if its length is 12 meters?

Write your answer in the box below.

44) $[-2 \times (-20) - 48] - (-20) + [2 \times 8] \div 4 = ?$

Write your answer in the box below.

45) What is the product of all possible values of x added to 30 in the following equation?
$|3x - 6| = 15$

Write your answer in the box below.

46) If $5x - 3 = 12$, what is the value of $4x + 12$?

Write your answer in the box below.

47) The average weight of 21 girls in a class is 45 kg and the average weight of 36 boys in the same class is 64 kg. What is the average weight of all the 57 students in that class?

Write your answer in the box below.

48) The width of a box is one third of its length. The height of the box is one half of its width. If the length of the box is 30 cm, what is the volume of the box?

Write your answer in the box below.

49) In a classroom of 40 students, 24 are female. What percentage of the class is male?

Write your answer in the box below.

50) Two third of 15 is equal to $\frac{5}{9}$ of what number?

Write your answer in the box below.

51) What is the value of x in the following equation?
$$-48 = 96 - x$$

Write your answer in the box below.

52) What is the value of the expression $2\left(x - 5\,y\right) + \left(3 - x\right)^2$ when $x = 3$ and $y = -2$?

Write your answer in the box below.

TASC Mathematics Practice Tests
Answer Keys

Now, it's time to review your results to see where you went wrong and what areas you need to improve.

TASC Practice Test 1

1)	A	2)	B	3)	A
4)	A	5)	D	6)	D
7)	A	8)	D	9)	A
10)	D	11)	B	12)	D
13)	A	14)	A	15)	B
16)	C	17)	D	18)	A
19)	A	20)	D	21)	C
22)	B	23)	C	24)	A
25)	A	26)	C	27)	A
28)	C	29)	D	30)	C
31)	D	32)	D	33)	A
34)	A	35)	A	36)	A
37)	B	38)	D	39)	B
40)	C	41)	26.75	42)	-2
43)	21	44)	220	45)	13
46)	3/2	47)	8	48)	7
49)	90	50)	150	51)	0.2
52)	33.75				

TASC Practice Test 2

1)	A	2)	B	3)	C
4)	C	5)	A	6)	B
7)	A	8)	D	9)	A
10)	A	11)	D	12)	C
13)	C	14)	A	15)	C
16)	B	17)	A	18)	A
19)	B	20)	A	21)	D
22)	D	23)	A	24)	B
25)	A	26)	C	27)	A
28)	D	29)	A	30)	D
31)	A	32)	C	33)	A
34)	A	35)	A	36)	A
37)	B	38)	A	39)	D
40)	B	41)	2.5	42)	1/3
43)	7	44)	18	45)	-15
46)	24	47)	57	48)	1500
49)	40%	50)	18	51)	144
52)	27				

TASC Mathematics Practice Tests
Answers and Explanations

TASC Mathematics Practice Test 1

1) Choice A is correct
Write the equation and solve for B:
0.50 A $= 0.25$ B, divide both sides by 0.25, then:
$0.65/0.25$ A $=$ B, therefore:
B $= 2$ A, and B is 2 times of A or it's 200% of A.

2) Choice B is correct
average $= \dfrac{sum\ of\ terms}{number\ of\ terms} = \dfrac{17 + 13 + 7 + 21 + 22}{5} = 805 = 16$

3) Choice A is correct
The average speed of john is: $180 \div 3 = 60$ km/h
The average speed of Alice is: $270 \div 9 = 30$ km/h
Write the ratio and simplify.
$60 : 30 \Rightarrow 2 : 1$

4) Choice A is correct
If the length of the box is 36, then the width of the box is one third of it, 12, and the height of the box is 4 (one third of the width).
The volume of the box is:
V $=$ lwh $= (36)\,(12)\,(4) = 1728$

5) Choice D is correct
Let x be the number.
Write the equation and solve for x.
$(25 - x) \div x = 4$
Multiply both sides by x.
$(25 - x) = 4\,x$, then add both sides.
$25 = 5\,x$, now divide both sides by 5.
$x = 5$

6) Choice D is correct
$7^4 = 7 \times 7 \times 7 \times 7 = 2,401$

206

7) Choice A is correct

Use percent formula: part $= \frac{percent}{100} \times$ whole

$27 = \frac{percent}{100} \times 30 \Rightarrow$

$27 = \frac{percent \times 30}{100} \Rightarrow$

$27 = \frac{percent \times 3}{10}$, multiply both sides by 10.

$270 = percent \times 3$, divide both sides by 3.

$90 = percent$

8) Choice D is correct

Use Pythagorean Theorem: $a^2 + b^2 = c^2$

$5^2 + 12^2 = c^2 \Rightarrow$

$25 + 144 = c^2 \Rightarrow$

$169 = c^2 \Rightarrow$

$c = 13$ cm

9) Choice A is correct

The sum of supplement angles is 180.

Let x be that angle.

Therefore, $x + 8x = 180$

$9x = 180$, divide both sides by 9 : $x = 20°$

10) Choice D is correct

Add the first 5 numbers.

$35 + 40 + 45 + 25 + 50 = 195$

To find the distance traveled in the next 5 hours, multiply the average by number of hours.

Distance $=$ Average $\times$ Rate $= 45 \times 5 = 225$

Add both numbers. $225 + 195 = 420$

11) Choice B is correct

$\$12 \times 8 = \$96$, Petrol use: $8 \times 2 = 16$ liters

Petrol cost: $16 \times \$1 = \$16$

Money earned: $\$96 - \$16 = \$80$

12) Choice D is correct

Use distance formula: Distance $=$ Rate $\times$ time $\Rightarrow 380 = 40 \times$ T, divide both sides by 40.

$380/40 =$ T $\Rightarrow$ T $= 9.5$ hours.

Change hours to minutes for the decimal part.

0.5 hours $= 0.5 \times 60 = 30$ minutes.

13) Choice A is correct

Use the formula for Percent of Change $\frac{New\ Value - Old\ Value}{old\ value} \times 100\%$

$\frac{25-50}{50} \times 100\% = -50\%$ (Negative sign here means that the new price is less than old price).

14) Choice A is correct

The ratio of boy to girls is $3 : 8$. Therefore, there are 3 boys out of 11 students.

To find the answer, first divide the total number of students by 11, then multiply the result by 3.

$55 \div 11 = 5 \Rightarrow 5 \times 3 = 15$

There are 15 boys and 30 $(55 - 15)$ girls.

So, 15 more boys should be enrolled to make the ratio $1 : 1$

15) Choice B is correct

The weight of 13.2 meters of this rope is: $13.3 \times 700\,g = 9,240\,g$

$1\,kg = 1,000\,g$, therefore, $9,240\,g \div 1000 = 9.24\,kg$

16) Choice C is correct

average $= \dfrac{sum\ of\ terms}{number\ of\ terms}$

The sum of the weight of all girls is: $15 \times 60 = 900\,kg$

The sum of the weight of all boys is: $30 \times 66 = 1,980\,kg$

The sum of the weight of all students is: $900 + 1,980 = 2,880\,kg$

average $= \dfrac{2,880}{45} = 64$

17) Choice D is correct

Find the product of two consecutive prime numbers:

$2 \times 3 = 6$ (not in the options)

$3 \times 5 = 15$ (bingo!)

$5 \times 7 = 35$ (not in the options)

$7 \times 11 = 77$ (not in the options)

18) Choice A is correct

Use this formula: Percent of Change $\frac{New\ Value - Old Value}{pld\ value} \times 100\%$

$\frac{18,000 - 20,000}{20,000} \times 100\% = 10\%$ and

$\frac{16,200 - 18,000}{18000} \times 100\% = 10\%$

Choice A is correct

The question is this: 560.50 is what percent of $1,121$?

Use percent formula:

part $= \frac{percent}{100} \times$ whole

19) $560.50 = \frac{percent}{100} \times 1,121 \Rightarrow 560.50 = \frac{percent \times 1,121}{100} \Rightarrow$

$56050 = percent \times 1.121 \Rightarrow$

percent $= \frac{56050}{1,121} = 50$

560.50 is 50% of $1,121$.

Therefore, the discount is: $100\% - 50\% = 50\%$

Choice D is correct

Let x be the original price.

20) If the price of the sofa is decreased by 15% to 748, then:

85% of $x = 748 \Rightarrow 0.85\ x = 748 \Rightarrow$

$x = 748 \div 0.85 = 880$

Choice C is correct

21) If the score of Mia was 90, therefore the score of Ava is 45.

Since, the score of Emma was one third as that of Ava, therefore, the score of Emma is 15.

Choice B is correct

Let x be the smallest number.

Then, these are the numbers:

$x, x + 1, x + 2, x + 3, x + 4$

22) average $= \frac{sum\ of\ terms}{number\ of\ terms}$

$\Rightarrow 32 = \frac{x + (x + 1) + (x + 2) + (x + 3) + (x + 4)}{5}$

$\Rightarrow 32 = \frac{5\ x + 10}{5} \Rightarrow 160 = 5\ x + 10 \Rightarrow 150 = 5x \Rightarrow x = 30$

Choice C is correct

23) Let x be the original price.

If the price of a laptop is decreased by 10% to 378, then:

90% of $x = 378 \Rightarrow 0.90\ x = 378 \Rightarrow x = 378 \div 0.90 = 420$

Choice A is correct

Write the numbers in order:

24) $4, 5, 8, 9, 13, 15, 18$

Since we have 7 numbers (7 is odd),

then the median is the number in the middle, which is 9.

Choice A is correct

25) The percent of girls playing tennis is:

$35\% \times 20\% = 0.35 \times 0.20 = 0.07 = 7\%$

Choice C is correct

Let x be the number.

Write the equation and solve for x.

26) $\frac{1}{3} \times 12 = \frac{2}{3} x$.

$x \Rightarrow \frac{1 \times 12}{3} = \frac{2x}{3}$, use cross multiplication to solve for x.

$3 \times 12 = 2x \times 3 \Rightarrow 36 = 6x \Rightarrow x = 6$

Choice A is correct

27) The area of the floor is: $8 \text{ cm} \times 35 \text{ cm} = 280 \text{ cm}^2$

The number of tiles needed $= 288 \div 10 = 28$

Choice C is correct

$$\begin{cases} x + 2y = 12 \\ 3x + 5y = 18 \end{cases} \rightarrow \text{Multiply the top equation by} -3 \text{ then,}$$

28) $$\begin{cases} -3x - 6y = -36 \\ 3x + 5y = 18 \end{cases} \rightarrow \text{Add two equations}$$

$-y = -18 \rightarrow y = 18$ plug in the value of y into the first equation

$x + 2y = 12 \rightarrow x + 2(18) = 12 \rightarrow x + 36 = 12$

Subtract 36 from both sides of the equation. Then: $x + 36 = 12 \rightarrow x = -24$

Choice D is correct

29) 5% of the volume of the solution is alcohol.

Let x be the volume of the solution.

Then: 5% of $x = 30 \text{ ml} \Rightarrow 0.05 x = 30 \Rightarrow x = 30 \div 0.05 = 600$

Choice C is correct

Formula for the Surface area of a cylinder is:

30) $SA = 2\pi r^2 + 2\pi r h \rightarrow 150\pi = 2\pi r^2 + 2\pi r (10)$

$\rightarrow r^2 + 10x - 75 = 0 \rightarrow (r + 15)(r - 5) = 0 \rightarrow r = 5 \text{ or } r = -15$

(unacceptable)

Choice D is correct

Let x be the number of years.

Therefore, $\$2,000$ per year equals $2000x$.

31) starting from $\$24,000$ annual salary means you should add that amount to $2000x$.

Income more than that is:

$I > 4000x + 21000$

32) Choice D is correct

Use simple interest formula: $I = prt$

(I = interest, p = principal, r = rate, t = time)

$I = (7,000)(0.04)(3) = 840$

33) Choice A is correct

Use the information provided in the question to draw the shape.

40 miles

Use Pythagorean Theorem: $a^2 + b^2 = c^2$

$40^2 + 30^2 = c^2 \Rightarrow 1600 + 900 = c^2 \Rightarrow 2500 = c^2 \Rightarrow c = 50$

34) Choice A is correct

If 17 balls are removed from the bag at random, there will be one ball in the bag.

The probability of choosing a brown ball is 1 out of 18.

Therefore, the probability of not choosing a brown ball is 17 out of 18 and the probability of having not a brown ball after removing 17 balls is the same.

35) Choice A is correct

Area of the circle is less than $49\,\pi$.

Use the formula of areas of circles.

Area $= \pi\,r^2 \Rightarrow 49\,\pi > \pi\,r^2 \Rightarrow$

$49 > r^2 \Rightarrow r < 7$

Radius of the circle is less than 7.

Let's put 7 for the radius.

Now, use the circumference formula:

Circumference $= 2\,\pi\,r = 2\,\pi\,(7) = 14\,\pi$

Since the radius of the circle is less than 7.

Then, the circumference of the circle must be less than $14\,\pi$.

Only choice A is less than $14\,\pi$.

36) Choice A is correct

Let's compare each fraction:

$\frac{2}{7} < \frac{3}{8} < \frac{5}{11} < \frac{3}{4}$

Only choice A provides the right order.

37) Choice B is correct

To find the discount, multiply the number by (100% − rate of discount).

Therefore, for the first discount we get: (D) $(100\% - 20\%) = $ (D) $(0.80) = 0.80$ D

For increase of 10% : $(0.85$ D$)(100\% + 10\%) = (0.85$ D$)(1.10) = 0.88$ D $= 88\%$ of D

211

Choice D is correct

38) To find the number of possible outfit combinations, multiply number of options for each factor: $7 \times 2 \times 5 = 70$

Choice B is correct

The equation of a line is in the form of $y = m x + b$, where m is the slope of the line and b is the $y-$intercept of the line.

Two points $(5, 3)$ and $(6, 4)$ are on line A.

Therefore, the slope of the line A is:

slope of line $A = \frac{y_2 - y_1}{x_2 - x_1} = \frac{4 - 3}{6 - 5} = \frac{1}{1} = 1$

The slope of line A is 1.

Thus, the formula of the line A is:

39) $y = x + b$, choose a point and plug in the values of x and y in the equation to solve for .

Let's choose point $(5, 3)$.

Then: $y = x + b \rightarrow 5 = 3 + b \rightarrow b = 5 - 3 = 2$

The equation of line A is: $y = x + 2$

Now, let's review the choices provided:

A. $(- 1, 2)$ $y = x + 2 \rightarrow 2 = - 1 + 2 = 1$ This is not true.

B. $(5, 7)$ $y = x + 2 \rightarrow 7 = 5 + 2 = 7$ This is true!

C. $(3, 4)$ $y = x + 2 \rightarrow 4 = 3 + 2 = 5$ This is not true.

D. $(- 1, - 2)$ $y = x + 2 \rightarrow - 2 = - 1 + 2 = 1$ This is not true.

Choice C is correct

The area of the trapezoid is: Area

40) $= \frac{1}{2} h (b1 + b2) = \frac{1}{2} (x)(13 + 8) = 126 \rightarrow 10.5 \, x = 126 \rightarrow x = 12$

$y = \sqrt{5^2 + 12^2} = \sqrt{25 + 144} = \sqrt{169} = 13$

The perimeter of the trapezoid is: $12 + 13 + 8 + 13 = 46$

The correct answer is 26.75

41) $2 x - 6 = 10.5 \rightarrow 2 x = 10.5 + 6 = 16.5 \rightarrow x = \frac{16.5}{2} = 8.25$

Then; $3 x + 2 = 3(8.25) + 2 = 24.75 + 2 = 26.75$

The correct answer is $- 2$

Use PEMDAS (order of operation):

$- 16 + 6 \times (- 5) - [6 + 22 \times (- 4)] \div 2 + 5 =$

42) $- 16 - 30 - [6 - 88] \div 2 + 5 =$

$- 43 - [- 82] \div 2 + 5 =$

$- 48 + 82 \div 2 + 5 =$

$- 48 + 41 + 5 = - 2$

43) The correct answer is 21

The input value is 3.

Then: $x = 3$, $f(x) = x^2 + 4x \rightarrow$

$f(3) = 9 + 4(3) = 9 + 12 = 21$

44) The correct answer is 220

The perimeter of the trapezoid is 58.

Therefore, the missing side (height) is $= 58 - 16 - 12 - 10 = 20$

Area of a trapezoid: $A = \frac{1}{2}h(b1 + b2) = \frac{1}{2}(20)(10 + 12) = 220$

45) The correct answer is 13

Since $N = 5$, substitute 5 for N in the equation $\frac{x+2}{3} = N$, which gives $\frac{x+2}{3} = 5$.

Multiplying both sides of $\frac{x+2}{3} = 5$ by 3 gives $x + 2 = 15$ and then adding -2 to both sides of

$x + 2 = 15$ then, $x = 13$.

46) The correct answer is $\frac{3}{2}$

Let x be the length of an edge of cube, then the volume of a cube is: $V = x^3$

The surface area of cube is: $A = 6x^2$

The volume of cube A is $\frac{1}{4}$ of its surface area. Then:

$x^3 = \frac{6x^2}{4} \rightarrow x^3 = \frac{3}{2}x^2$, divide both side of the equation by x^2.

Then: $\frac{x^3}{x^2} = \frac{3x^2}{2x^2} \rightarrow x = \frac{3}{2}$

47) The correct answer is 8

First draw an isosceles triangle.

Remember that two sides of the triangle are equal.

Let put a for the legs. Then:

$a = 4 \Rightarrow$ area of the triangle is $= \frac{1}{2}(4 \times 4) = \frac{16}{2} = 8$

48) The correct answer is 7

$\text{average} = \frac{sum\ of\ terms}{number\ of\ terms} \Rightarrow$

$15 = \frac{13 + 16 + 24 + x}{4} \Rightarrow$

$60 = 53 + x \Rightarrow x = 7$

49) The correct answer is $90°$

The relationship among all sides of special right triangle
$30° - 60° - 90°$ is provided in this triangle:

In this triangle, the opposite side of $30°$ angle is half of the hypotenuse.

Draw the shape of this question.

The latter is the hypotenuse.

Therefore, the latter is **90** feet.

50) The correct answer is 150

The question is this: 1.95 is what percent of 1.30?

Use percent formula:

$\text{part} = \frac{percent}{100} \times \text{whole}$

$1.95 = \frac{percent}{100} \times 1.30 \Rightarrow 1.95 = \frac{percent \times 1.30}{100} \Rightarrow 195 = \text{percent} \times 1.30 \Rightarrow \text{percent}$
$= \frac{195}{1.30} = 150$

51) The correct answer is $\frac{1}{5}$ or 0.2

Write the ratio of $3\,a$ to $4\,b$.

$\frac{3\,a}{6\,b} = \frac{1}{10}$

Use cross multiplication and then simplify.

$3\,a \times 10 = 6\,b \times 1 \rightarrow 30\,a = 6\,b \rightarrow a = \frac{6\,b}{30} = \frac{b}{5}$

Now, find the ratio of a to b.

$\frac{a}{b} = \frac{\frac{b}{5}}{b} \rightarrow \frac{b}{5} \div b = \frac{b}{5} \times \frac{1}{b} = \frac{b}{5\,b} = \frac{1}{5} = 0.2$

52) The correct answer is 33.75 m

The rate of construction company $= \frac{50\ cm}{1\ min} = 50$ cm/min

Height of the wall after 45 minutes $= \frac{50\ cm}{1\ min} \times 45$ min $= 2,250$ cm

Let x be the height of wall, then $\frac{2}{3}\,x = 2,250$ cm $\rightarrow x = \frac{3 \times 2,250}{2} \rightarrow x = 3,375$ cm
$= 33.75$ m

TASC Mathematics Practice Tests
Answers and Explanations

TASC Mathematics Practice Test 2

1) Choice A is correct
Volume of a box = Length × width × height = $3 \times 5 \times 8 = 120$

2) Choice B is correct
$x + 3y = 8$.
Plug in the values of x and y from choices provided. Then:
A. $(-2, 3)$ $x + 3y = 8 \rightarrow -2 + 3(3) = 8 \rightarrow -2 + 9 = 7$ This is NOT true.
B. $(2, 2)$ $x + 3y = 8 \rightarrow 2 + 3(2) = 8 \rightarrow 2 + 6 = 8$ This is true!
C. $(-2, 3)$ $x + 3y = 8 \rightarrow -2 + 3(3) = 8 \rightarrow -2 + 9 = 7$ This is NOT true.
D. $(-3, 4)$ $x + 3y = 8 \rightarrow -3 + 3(4) = 8 \rightarrow -3 + 12 = 9$ This is NOT true.

3) Choice C is correct
Three times of $20,000$ is $60,000$.
One fifth of them cancelled their tickets.
One fifth of $60,000$ equals $12,000$ ($\frac{1}{5} \times 60,000 = 12000$).
$48,000$ ($60,000 - 12,000 = 48,000$) fans are attending this week

4) Choice C is correct
To get a sum of 6 for two dice, we can get 5 different options:
$(5, 1), (4, 2), (3, 3), (2, 4), (1, 5)$
To get a sum of 9 for two dice, we can get 4 different options:
$(6, 3), (5, 4), (4, 5), (3, 6)$
Therefore, there are 9 options to get the sum of 6 or 9.
Since, we have $6 \times 6 = 36$ total options, the probability of getting a sum of 6 and 9 is 9 out of 36 or $\frac{1}{4}$.

5) Choice A is correct
$4^5 = 4 \times 4 \times 4 \times 4 \times 4 = 1,024$

6) Choice B is correct
The diagonal of the square is 10.
Let x be the side.
Use Pythagorean Theorem: $a^2 + b^2 = c^2$
$x^2 + x^2 = 10^2 \Rightarrow$
$2\,x^2 = 10^2 \Rightarrow 2\,x^2 = 100 \Rightarrow x^2 = 50 \Rightarrow x = \sqrt{50}$
The area of the square is: $\sqrt{50} \times \sqrt{50} = 50$

7) Choice A is correct
Write the numbers in order: $7, 19, 25, 29, 35, 44, 63$
Median is the number in the middle.
So, the median is 29.

8) Choice D is correct
Use Pythagorean Theorem:
$a^2 + b^2 = c^2$
$5^2 + 12^2 = c^2 \Rightarrow 169 = c^2 \Rightarrow c = 13$

9) Choice A is correct
Plug in 104 for F and then solve for C.
$C = \frac{3}{5}\,(F - 29) \Rightarrow C = \frac{3}{5}\,(104 - 29) \Rightarrow C = \frac{3}{5}\,(75) = 45$

10) Choice A is correct
$(4\,x^3 + 3\,x^2 - 4\,x^4) - (2\,x^2 + 3\,x^4 - 5\,x^3) \Rightarrow$
$(4\,x^3 + 3\,x^2 - 4\,x^4) - 2\,x^2 - 3\,x^4 + 5\,x^3 \Rightarrow$
$9\,x^3 + x^2 - 7\,x^4$

11) Choice D is correct
Let x be the number.
Write the equation and solve for x.
36% of $x = 9 \Rightarrow 0.36\,x = 6 \Rightarrow x = 9 \div 0.36 = 25$

12) Choice C is correct
Change the numbers to decimal and then compare.
$\frac{1}{3} = 0.333...$
0.82
$55\% = 0.55$
$\frac{4}{9} = 0.444...$
Then: $\frac{1}{3} < \frac{4}{9} < 55\% < 0.82$

Choice C is correct

13) Let x be all expenses, then $\frac{22}{100} x = \$616 \to x = \frac{100 \times \$616}{22} = \$2,800$

He spent for his rent: $\frac{27}{100} \times \$2,800 = \$756$

Choice A is correct

The distance between Jason and Joe is 9 miles.

14) Jason running at 5.5 miles per hour and Joe is running at the speed of 7 miles per hour. Therefore, every hour the distance is 1.5 miles less.

$9 \div 1.5 = 6$

Choice C is correct

The failing rate is 12 out of $60 = \frac{12}{60}$

15) Change the fraction to percent: $\frac{12}{60} \times 100\% = 20\%$

20 percent of students failed.

Therefore, 80 percent of students passed the exam.

Choice B is correct

Use simple interest formula: $I = prt$

16) ($I =$ interest, $p =$ principal, $r =$ rate, $t =$ time)

$I = (15000)(0.045)(2) = 1350$

Choice A is correct

17) $3 x^2 y^3 (4 x^2 y)^3 =$

$3 x^2 y^3 (64 x^6 y^3) = 192 x^8 y^6$

Choice A is correct

Let x be the number of new shoes the team can purchase. Therefore, the team can purchase $150 x$.

18) The team had $\$21,000$ and spent $\$12,000$.

Now the team can spend on new shoes $\$9,000$ at most.

Now, write the inequality: $150 x + 12,000 \leq 21,000$

Choice B is correct

19) The probability of choosing a Hearts is $\frac{12}{54} = \frac{1}{6}$

20) Choice A is correct
The population is increased by 15% and 20%.
15% increase changes the population to 115% of original population.
For the second increase, multiply the result by 120%.
$(1.15) \times (1.20) = 1.38 = 138\%$
38 percent of the population is increased after two years.

21) Choice D is correct
First, find the sum of five numbers.
average $= \frac{sum\ of\ terms}{number\ of\ terms} \Rightarrow$
$26.4 = \frac{sum\ of\ 5numbers}{5} \Rightarrow$
sum of 5 numbers $= 26.4 \times 5 = 132$
The sum of 5 numbers is 135.
If a sixth number that is greater than 42 is added to these numbers, then the sum of 6 numbers must be greater than 174.
$132 + 42 = 174$
If the number was 42, then the average of the numbers is:
average $= \frac{sum\ of\ terms}{number\ of\ terms} = \frac{174}{6} = 29$
Since the number is bigger than 42.
Then, the average of six numbers must be greater than 29.
Choice D is greater than 29.

22) Choice D is correct
Surface Area of a cylinder $= 2\pi r (r + h)$
The radius of the cylinder is 3 ($6 \div 2$) inches and its height is 8 inches. Therefore,
Surface Area of a cylinder $= 2\pi (3)(3 + 8) = 66\pi$

23) Choice A is correct
The square of a number is $\frac{36}{64}$, then the number is the square root of $\frac{36}{64}$
$\sqrt{\frac{36}{64}} = \frac{6}{8}$
The cube of the number is: $(\frac{6}{8})^3 = \frac{216}{512}$

24) Choice B is correct
Probability $= \frac{number\ of\ desired\ outcomes}{number\ of\ total\ outcomes} = \frac{18}{12+18+18+24} = \frac{18}{72} = \frac{1}{4}$

25) Choice A is correct
The perimeter of the trapezoid is 45 cm.
Therefore, the missing side (height) is $= 45 - 15 - 10 - 8 = 12$
Area of a trapezoid: $A = \frac{1}{2} h (a + b) = \frac{1}{2}(10)(15 + 12) = 135 \text{ cm}^2$

26) Choice C is correct
First, find the number.
Let x be the number.
Write the equation and solve for x.
130% of a number is 65, then:
$1.3 \times x = 65 \Rightarrow x = 65 \div 1.3 = 50$
84% of 50 is: $0.84 \times 50 = 42$

27) Choice A is correct
Isolate and solve for x.
$\frac{2}{5} x + \frac{1}{4} = \frac{1}{2} \Rightarrow$
$\frac{2}{5} x = \frac{1}{2} - \frac{1}{4} \Rightarrow$
$\frac{2}{5} x = \frac{1}{4}$
$\frac{2x}{5} = \frac{1}{4} \Rightarrow 2 x \times 4 = 5 \times 1$
$8 x = 5 \Rightarrow x = \frac{5}{8}$

28) Choice D is correct
Jason needs an 75% average to pass for five exams.
Therefore, the sum of 5 exams must be at lease $5 \times 75 = 375$
The sum of 4 exams is: $64 + 55 + 82 + 80 = 281$
The minimum score Jason can earn on his fifth and final test to pass is: $375 - 281 = 94$

29) Choice A is correct
$2,800$ out of $56,000$ equals to $\frac{2800}{56000} = \frac{28}{560} = \frac{1}{20}$

30) Choice D is correct
$-2 + 4 \leq 2 x - 4 + 4 < 8 + 4 \Rightarrow$
$2 \leq 2 x < 12 \Rightarrow$ (divide all sides by 2) $1 \leq x < 6$
x is between 1 and 6.
Choice D represent this inequality.

31)

Choice A is correct

Let L be the length of the rectangular and W be the with of the rectangular.

Then, $L = 3W + 4$

The perimeter of the rectangle is 56 meters.

Therefore: $2W + 2L = 56$

$W + L = 28$

Replace the value of L from the first equation into the second equation and solve for

$L: (3W + 4) + L = 28 \rightarrow 4W + 4 = 28 \rightarrow 4W = 24 \rightarrow W = 6$

The width of the rectangle is 3 meters and its length is:

$L = 3W + 4 = 3(6) + 4 = 22$

The area of the rectangle is: length $\times$ width $= 22 \times 6 = 132$

32)

Choice C is correct

The ratio of boy to girls is $3 : 9$.

Therefore, there are 3 boys out of 12 students.

To find the answer, first divide the total number of students by 12, then multiply the result by 3.

$48 \div 12 = 4 \Rightarrow 4 \times 3 = 12$

There are 12 boys and 36 $(48 - 12)$ girls.

So, 24 more boys should be enrolled to make the ratio $1 : 1$

33)

Choice A is correct

The area of the square is 595.36.

Therefore, the side of the square is square root of the area. $\sqrt{561.69} = 23.7$

Four times the side of the square is the perimeter: $4 \times 23.7 = 94.8$

34)

Choice A is correct

Solving Systems of Equations by Elimination

Multiply the first equation by (-2), then add it to the second equation.

$-2(2x + 4y = 18)$

$\underline{4x - y = -9} \Rightarrow$

$-4x - 8y = -36$

$\underline{4x - y = -9}$

$-9y = -45$

$\Rightarrow y = 5$

Plug in the value of y into one of the equations and solve for x.

$2x + 4(5) = 18 \Rightarrow 2x = -20 + 18 \Rightarrow 2x = -2 \Rightarrow x = -1$

Choice A is correct

In the stadium the ratio of home fans to visiting fans in a crowd is $4 : 9$.

Therefore, total number of fans must be divisible by $13 : 4 + 9 = 13$.

Let's review the choices:

35) A. $12,324 \div 13 = 948$

B. $42,326 \div 13 = 3,255.846$

C. $44,566 \div 13 = 3,428.153$

D. $66,812 \div 13 = 5,139.386$

Only choice A when divided by 13 results a whole number.

Choice A is correct

average $= \frac{sum\ of\ terms}{number\ of\ terms} \Rightarrow$

36) (average of 6 numbers) $24 = \frac{sum\ of\ numbers}{6} \Rightarrow$ sum of 6 numbers is $24 \times 6 = 144$

(average of 4 numbers) $12 = \frac{sum\ of\ numbers}{4} \Rightarrow$ sum of 4 numbers is $12 \times 4 = 48$

sum of 6 numbers $-$ sum of 4 numbers $=$ sum of 2 numbers $144 - 48 = 96$

average of 2 numbers $= \frac{96}{2} = 48$

Choice B is correct

Use formula of rectangle prism volume.

37) V $=$ (Length) (width) (height) $\Rightarrow$

$2,500 = (25)(20)$ (height)

$\Rightarrow$ height $= 2,500 \div 500 = 5$

Choice A is correct

average (mean) $= \frac{sum\ of\ terms}{number\ of\ terms} \Rightarrow$

$80 = \frac{sum\ of\ terms}{40} \Rightarrow$

38) sum $= 80 \times 40 = 3,200$

The difference of 92 and 64 is 28.

Therefore, 28 should be subtracted from the sum.

$3,200 - 28 = 3,172$

mean $= \frac{sum\ of\ terms}{number\ of\ terms} \Rightarrow$ mean $= \frac{3,172}{40} = 79.3$

Choice D is correct

The width of the rectangle is twice its length.

Let x be the length.

39) Then, width $= 2x$

Perimeter of the rectangle is 2 (width $+$ length)

$= 2(2x + x) = 120 \Rightarrow 6x = 120 \Rightarrow x = 20$

Length of the rectangle is 20 meters.

Choice B is correct

40) To find the number of possible outfit combinations, multiply number of options for each factor: $3 \times 4 \times 6 = 72$

The correct answer is 2.5
Write a proportion and solve for the missing number.

41) $\frac{38.4}{12} = \frac{8}{x} \rightarrow$
$38.4\, x = 8 \times 12 = 96$
$38.4\, x = 96 \rightarrow x = \frac{96}{38.4} = 2.5$

The correct answer is $\frac{1}{3}$
The equation of a line in slope intercept form is: $y = m\, x + c$
Solve for y.

42) $3\, x + 2\, y = 8 \rightarrow y = -3\, x + 8$
The slope of this line is -3.
The product of the slopes of two perpendicular lines is -1.
Therefore, the slope of a line that is perpendicular to this line is:
$m_1 \times m_2 = -1 \Rightarrow -3 \times m_2 = -1 \Rightarrow m_2 = \frac{-1}{-3} = \frac{1}{3}$

The correct answer is 7

43) Let y be the width of the rectangle.
Then; $12 \times y = 84 \rightarrow y = \frac{84}{12} = 7$

The correct answer is 18

44) $[-2 \times (-20) - 48] - (-20) + [2 \times 8] \div 4 =$
$[40 - 48] + 20 + 16 \div 4 =$
$-6 + 20 + 4 = 18$

The correct answer is -15
To solve absolute values equations, write two equations.

45) $3\, x - 6$ can equal positive 15, or negative 15.
Therefore, $3\, x - 6 = 15 \Rightarrow 3\, x = 21 \Rightarrow x = 7$
$3\, x - 6 = -15 \Rightarrow 3\, x = -15 + 6 = -9 \Rightarrow x = -3$
Find the product of solutions: $-3 \times 15 = -45, -45 + 30 = -15$

The correct answer is 24

46) $5\, x - 3 = 12 \rightarrow 5\, x = 12 + 3 = 15 \rightarrow x = \frac{15}{5} \rightarrow x = 3$
Then, $4\, x + 12 = 4\,(3) + 12 = 12 + 12 = 24$

47) The correct answer is 57 kg

$\text{Average} = \frac{sum\ of\ terms}{number\ of\ terms}$

The sum of the weight of all girls is: $21 \times 45 = 945$ kg
The sum of the weight of all boys is: $36 \times 64 = 2,304$ kg
The sum of the weight of all students is: $945 + 2,304 = 3,249$ kg

$\text{Average} = \frac{3249,}{57} = 57$

48) The correct answer is $1,500$ cm^3

If the length of the box is 30, then the width of the box is one third of it, 10, and the height of the box is 5 (one half of the width).

The volume of the box is: $V = IWH = (30)(10)(5) = 1,500$ cm^3

49) The correct answer is 40%

Number of males in classroom is: $40 - 24 = 16$

Then, the percentage of males in the classroom is: $\frac{16}{40} \times 100 = 0.4 \times 100 = 40\%$

50) The correct answer is 18

Let x be the number.

Write the equation and solve for x.

$\frac{2}{3} \times 15 = \frac{5}{9} x \rightarrow \frac{2 \times 15}{3} = \frac{5\,x}{9}$, use cross multiplication to solve for x.

$9 \times 30 = 5\,x \times 3 \Rightarrow 270 = 15\,x \Rightarrow x = 18$

51) The correct answer is 144

$-48 = 96 - x$, First, subtract 96 from both sides of the equation.

Then: $-48 - 96 = 96 - 96 - x \rightarrow -144 = -x$

Multiply both sides by $(-1):\ \rightarrow x = 144$

52) The correct answer is 27

Plug in the value of x and y.

$2(x - 5y) + (3 - x)^2$ when $x = 3$ and $y = -2$

$x = 3$ and $y = -2$

$2(x - 5y) + (3 - x)^2 =$

$2(3 - 5(-2)) + (3 - 2)^2 =$

$2(3 + 10) + (1)^2 = 26 + 1 = 27$

Receive the PDF version of this book or get another FREE book!

Thank you for using our Book!

Do you LOVE this book?

Then, you can get the PDF version of this book or another book absolutely FREE!

Please email us at:

info@Testinar.com

for details.

Made in the USA
Monee, IL
13 October 2020